"You are ⌐ **croaked** ⌐.

"You sound almost surprised," Jamie murmured blandly. "Which is odd, considering I still appear to be the selfish, manipulative tearaway you claim to know so well. Though there is one thing that puzzles me, Jenny...with so little going for me, how is it that you managed to develop such an almighty crush on me?"

KATE PROCTOR is part Irish and part Welsh, though she spent most of her childhood in England and several years of her adult life in central Africa. She now lives just outside London with her two cats, Florence and Minnie (presented to her by her daughters, who live fairly close by). Having given up her career as a teacher on her return to England, Kate now devotes most of her time to writing.

Kate Proctor

TWO-TIMING LOVE

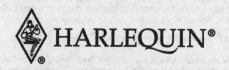

HARLEQUIN®

TORONTO • NEW YORK • LONDON
AMSTERDAM • PARIS • SYDNEY • HAMBURG
STOCKHOLM • ATHENS • TOKYO • MILAN • MADRID
PRAGUE • WARSAW • BUDAPEST • AUCKLAND

ISBN 0-373-18781-5

TWO-TIMING LOVE

First North American Publication 2002.

CHAPTER ONE

'I was beginning to think you'd never turn up—have you brought the documents?'

Jennifer Page froze at the sound of that voice, the warm, creamy tones of her normally vibrantly attractive features dulling to pallor as she resisted the urge to drag her fingers through the gleaming auburn of her short, almost boyishly cropped hair—a habit she knew to be triggered off by feelings of stress. And stress was decidedly what she was experiencing now, even as she hoped against hope that her imagination was in the throes of playing the nastiest trick it possibly could on her. But it was a pale imitation of her normally sunny smile that she bestowed on the hotel porter as he deposited her overnight case on the floor beside her.

Her movements almost robotic, Jenny turned to face the tall, powerfully built figure of the man who had addressed her, myriad sensations bombarding her and precious few of them in the least pleasant.

'I haven't any Austrian money—would you mind tipping the porter?' she muttered stiltedly, one part of her strenuously denying that this was happening to her while the rest responded with nerve-jangling awareness to the familiar, larger-than-life figure of Jamie Castile.

She had almost forgotten how disgustingly attractive he was, she thought, weak with disbelief; but not the aura of danger emanating so powerfully from that faultlessly built masculine body now taking oddly tentative steps towards her.

She frowned in puzzlement as he halted before the

5

porter, conscious that his movements lacked their customary languid grace as he fumbled awkwardly in his pocket and then handed the man some money. It was as he turned slightly towards her that Jenny let out a soft groan of disbelief and leaned heavily against the wall for support.

Perhaps the dimness of the room's lighting accounted for her having missed it—that swaddled mound nestling against one broad shoulder and so obviously hampering the flow of his movements.

'Well?' demanded Jamie, his grey-green eyes offering no hint of welcome as the porter closed the door of the suite behind him. 'Did you bring all the papers?'

'Yes,' replied Jenny, attempting to clear her mind of the shock and disbelief threatening to paralyse it. 'Where are Clare and Graham?'

'They're still in Czechoslovakia with the other doctors—trying to do what they can for the earthquake victims.'

'But...I...' Jenny threw up her hands in exasperation with herself as the words refused to come. 'Would you mind telling me what's going on?' she exclaimed, an edge of desperation in her tone.

Jamie Castile gave an impatient shrug, a gesture he plainly regretted the instant he had made it as the bundle against his shoulder stirred and let out a wail of protest that brought a look of weary sufferance to his handsome features.

'For God's sake, take it, will you?' he groaned, gingerly removing the baby from against him and holding it out to her.

Jenny took an involuntary step back from the now vociferously protesting bundle that was their four-month-old nephew.

'I...I'm not used to babies,' she stammered.

'For God's sake, try something, can't you?' exploded Jamie. 'Once it decides to start screeching like this there's nothing I can do with it.'

'Stop calling him it!' hissed Jenny, taking the proffered bundle awkwardly into her arms and gazing down at it with a mixture of awe and trepidation. 'Hello, little Jonathan Page,' she whispered, her tentative smile accentuating the delicate beauty of her features as the infant quietened and fixed her with a wide-eyed gaze. 'It's late—shouldn't he be in his bed and asleep?' she demanded accusingly of his uncle.

'I'm sure he should,' drawled Jamie, flinging his tall frame heavily on to one of the perilously dainty chairs dotted around the room. 'But actually achieving that requires skills I obviously don't possess.'

Though ones he clearly expected her to have in abundance, simply because she was female, thought Jenny exasperatedly, then cuddled the baby to her with a small pang of guilt as he let out an ear-piercing wail. It wasn't his fault his little life had suddenly been turned upside-down and it certainly wasn't going to make him feel secure hearing his uncle and aunt indulging in a slanging match.

'Which room is he in?' she asked briskly.

Jamie's reply was to nod in the general direction of one of the doors leading off the room.

The cot, next to an outsized double bed, looked slightly incongruous in contrast to the opulence of the room, as did too the jumble of disposable nappies and baby clothes strewn over the bed.

Jenny unwrapped the shawl from around her tiny nephew, whom she had last seen at his christening over a month ago—after which his parents had taken him back to Brussels, where they were part of an international medical team.

'It's lovely to see you again, even though it's all a bit of a shock,' she crooned as she placed him gently in the cot and tucked the covers around him. She winced as he let out another of those ear-piercing yells, then began patting him soothingly on his tiny back. 'Be a good boy and go to sleep,' she pleaded, her hand still patting gently.

After ten minutes, she crept out of the room, unconsciously holding her breath.

Jamie was still sprawled on the chair, an expression of scowling exhaustion on his face as his gaze met hers.

'I wouldn't bother sitting down, if I were you,' he informed her as she made to do precisely that. 'It'll start bellowing any second now.'

'His name is Jonathan!' snapped Jenny, confusion and her own exhaustion adding aggression to her tone.

She sat down, her wide-spaced blue eyes meeting his in open defiance as she silently prayed the baby wouldn't waken.

'Jamie, would you mind explaining what's going on?'

He raised a hand to his head and began running his fingers absent-mindedly through the dark thickness of his hair. It was a gesture suddenly so achingly familiar to her that Jenny found herself dropping her gaze to escape it.

'I left messages all over the place for you,' he accused inconsequentially. 'Jenny, where the hell have you been—and where are your parents?'

'I work in London now and my parents are in New Zealand—they left last week,' she replied, determined to keep calm. She was a fully fledged adult now, she reminded herself sharply, and there was no way she would ever let Jamie Castile get under her skin again—ever! 'And as for your leaving me messages all over the place—I was under the impression they came from Clare and Graham.'

There was mocking amusement in the glance he gave her.

'The implication being that you'd have ignored any message emanating from me, is that it, Jenny?'

'For heaven's sake, Jamie, be serious!' she exclaimed, mortified to feel the hot colour flooding her cheeks. 'When I got a message asking that I bring copies of Graham's and Clare's birth and marriage certificates here I assumed they'd lost their passports in the earthquake...I was worried!'

'I can't imagine why,' drawled Jamie. 'The medical conference they were attending was in Bratislava, which experienced no more than the mild rumbles registered here in Vienna.'

'So why do they need all those documents?' demanded Jenny exasperatedly. 'I was under the impression they were stranded in Czechoslovakia!'

'It's more a case of the baby being stranded,' replied Jamie. 'Though why the hell they insist on carting a child that young around with them is beyond me.'

'I think it's wonderful that they can do it,' retorted Jenny. 'Obviously the best place for him is with his parents.'

'And obviously that's precisely where he can't be right now,' pointed out Jamie infuriatingly. 'Getting him out of Czechoslovakia and into Austria didn't present too many problems—I collected him from Clare the day before yesterday.'

Jenny bit back a comment on how Clare must have felt—having to hand her infant son into the care of a brother few would describe as either predictable or dependable.

'The authorities at the British Embassy here in Vienna

have agreed to issue temporary travel documents for the child—on production of the papers you've brought with you,' he continued. 'So you won't have any problems getting him into England.'

'I beg your pardon?' croaked Jenny.

'Clare seemed to think your parents would look after him till she and Graham felt free to leave...obviously they weren't aware they'd taken off for New Zealand.'

'They weren't going till the New Year, but then they decided...Jamie, all this is beside the point!' she exclaimed frustratedly. 'There's no one to look after him in England...unless your mother—'

'I believe my mother's off on one of her jaunts,' he interrupted impatiently. 'And besides, you know how vague she can be—which is why Clare didn't even bother trying to contact her and got on to me instead.'

'Precisely—she left him with you,' observed Jenny decisively. 'And now that I've brought you the necessary documents you'll have no problem getting him back to England.'

'I'm not going back to England,' he informed her icily. 'I was just about to catch a flight for Brazil when your brother rang—right at this very moment I'm supposed to be doing trial runs on a new boat I've entered in an important race—'

'And you'd rather play with your boats than see to your nephew's well-being—'

'You know damned well I don't *play* with boats—I design and race them,' he informed her coldly. 'And a lot of skilled men depend on my designing and racing abilities for their living.'

'And I suppose that I, being a mere woman, couldn't possibly have a job of any importance!' exclaimed Jenny, perilously close to losing her temper. 'Well, it so happens that I have. I only started it a couple of weeks ago and I've already put it in jeopardy by dashing off here at a moment's notice. And I've lost the flat I was hoping to move into—thanks to having to chase all over the place getting those papers—so if you think—'

'Give it a rest, will you, Jenny?' drawled Jamie dismissively, getting to his feet. 'Because, after two nights without a wink of sleep, I'm not in the least receptive to any sob-story you choose to come up with.'

'Choose to come up with?' shrieked Jenny, beside herself with rage as she too leapt to her feet. 'Jamie Castile, just who the hell do you think you—?'

The two of them froze as the baby's piercing cries reached their ears.

'You're the one who woke it with your histrionics,' muttered Jamie, striding towards the second of the doors leading off the room, 'so you can damned well deal with it.'

'My God, you're all gentleman, aren't you?' she flung after him.

He turned as he reached the door.

'And you, my dear Jennifer, are one woman supremely qualified to vouch for that fact,' he murmured mockingly.

Her face burning with humiliation, Jenny turned on her heel and marched into the room containing her protesting nephew. Trust him to throw that up at her, she fumed to herself, under no illusion as to what his taunt had referred, then forcefully hurled all thought of the subject from her mind.

'Poor little man,' she whispered, her face softening as she picked up the distraught baby and cradled him to her. 'Are you missing your mummy and daddy?'

He quietened miraculously in her arms and remained silent as she laid him on the bed and made an attempt to inspect his nappy.

'Why—you little rascal!' she laughed, as his face broke into a lop-sided smile and he began gurgling with contentment. 'You just wanted some attention, didn't you?'

Tiny feet began pummelling at her ribcage, dislodging the nappy she was clumsily trying secure around him.

'Jonathan, you'll have to co-operate,' she protested with a chuckle. 'This is my first encounter with the mysteries of nappy-changing!'

The instant she tried returning him to his cot, he protested deafeningly. In the end she gave up trying and lay down on the bed with her nephew lying in angelic peacefulness against her.

She closed her eyes, a feeling of total mental and physical exhaustion wafting through her. She had gone to work early that morning and had worked flat out to clear what she could from her desk—just in case she didn't make it back to London at a reasonable hour tomorrow.

She gave a soft groan of dismay as she remembered the icy response with which her unorthodox request for a day off—possibly two—had been met. She was still at the stage of waking each morning unable to believe she actually had landed the job of her dreams with Wardale's, one of the most dynamic and prestigious advertising companies around…and now, in her first month and in the vital preliminary period of an important campaign in which she had to prove herself, she was taking time off!

A rueful grin crept over her face as she found herself switching her thoughts towards Jamie. Never in her entire twenty-three years had she thought the day would come when she would regard concentrating her thoughts on Jamie as the lesser of two evils!

For the best part of four years she had just about managed to erase him from her mind, she reminded herself with drowsy detachment. And it had probably taken the best part of that time to cure her of her obsession with him, she admitted with reluctance. As a child she had openly hero-worshipped him, dazzled by the recklessly adventurous spirit of the godlike creature who was almost eight years her senior and her older brother's closest friend. Child and man, Jamie Castile was one who regarded life as something to be lived to the hilt—and live it to the hilt he had done with a total disregard to either convention or his own personal safety.

'That Castile boy's been allowed to run wild for far too long—he'll come to no good,' had been the oft-voiced opinion in the small Sussex village in which they had both been born...yet there had always been a note of grudging admiration—pride almost—behind the words.

And Jamie, with his strange background of opulence and poverty, had turned their dire predictions upside-down. Never one to compromise, he had thrown himself heart and soul into what he loved most, racing and designing yachts. The fact that he had made a considerable fortune from what he so loved had probably been of scant consequence to him initially, although, judging by his earlier remarks, he now seemed fully aware of his responsibilities towards those deriving their livelihoods from the fortune his skills had brought him.

It was around the time she was fifteen that she had stopped bemoaning the fact she hadn't been born a boy and that her heart had begun doing strange things whenever Jamie was around. At sixteen, finding herself plotting painfully lingering deaths for any female who caught his attention—a veritable army, for Jamie's eye roved far and wide—she had finally faced up to the fact that the hero-worship of her earlier years had matured to love. And with a maturity far beyond her years she had bided her time, the woman's heart within her adolescent body vacillating between despair and relief as a daunting procession of rivals caught and then lost the attention of his restlessly roving eye.

Three years later, on the night of her brother's wedding to Jamie's sister, she had decided, at nineteen, that even Jamie could no longer regard her as a child. That night—a full four years ago—the brutal totality with which he had rejected her naïvely explicit advances had devastated her; and today had been the first time she had so much as laid eyes on him since. She was cured of her obsessive love of him, but the savage wound he had inflicted on her pride had left a scar that she now realised would always be with her.

'Jenny?'

As her eyes flew open they found Jamie standing in the doorway, a small circular tray balanced on one hand.

'He kept crying each time I tried to put him in his cot,' she explained defensively, thrown by the flash of pure hatred the sight of him had sent searing through her. She struggled upright, the soundly sleeping baby clasped to her.

'He's just about due for another feed,' stated Jamie, approaching the bed, then sitting down on it.

'Did you make it up for him?' asked Jenny, forcing her mind back to the present as she glanced down at the two bottles on the tray he had placed on the bed—one filled with milk, the other apparently containing water.

The darkly defined curves of his eyebrows rose in pained disbelief. 'Mercifully, it's a service the hotel provides. Clare gave me a few tins of the formula and sheets of instructions—which you'll no doubt need.'

Jenny's sharp exclamation of impatience brought a

whimper of protest from the bundle in her arms—a whimper that fast developed into a full-blooded yell.

'I think you'd better feed him now,' she said, placing the bellowing infant in his arms and jumping to her feet as he showed signs of wanting to pass him back. 'And, at the risk of sounding repetitive,' she stated firmly, 'Jamie, I really do have to be back at work by tomorrow, if possible.'

'Surely they can give you a bit of time off, in the circumstances,' he exclaimed, deftly transferring the baby to the crook of his arm and testing the temperature of the milk in the bottle before proceeding with the feed with a casual air of expertise that took Jenny's breath away. 'After all, it is your brother's baby—'

'And *your* sister's!' she cut in exasperatedly, drawing up a chair and sitting down. 'Which is all beside the point. Jamie, I've only been in this job for a couple of weeks…it's one in a million, as far as I'm concerned, and I don't want to jeopardise it.'

He glanced up from the baby and pulled a wry face.

'One in a million, eh?'

Jenny nodded. 'And I'm on an initial three months' trial.'

'It seems as though we have a bit of a problem on our hands,' he muttered, then suddenly removed the bottle from the baby and hoisted him up on his shoulder, pummelling him vigorously on the back.

'Jamie, don't you think you're being a bit rough with him?' she gasped.

'Stop trying to teach your grandmother how to suck eggs,' he retorted with a grin that became a chuckle when the baby obligingly burped with gusto. 'He's a tough little tyke,' he laughed, transferring the baby back into his arms and resuming the feed.

Jenny raised her hand to her mouth in an attempt to

hide the disbelieving laughter mounting within her—she would have given anything for a camera, preferably a cine.

'And you can stop smirking, clever clogs,' he warned, 'because it isn't nearly as simple as it looks. The first two feeds were sheer hell, until I got the knack...as you'll soon find out.'

'Jamie, how many times do I have to tell you?' she exclaimed in exasperation, all trace of laughter gone. 'I *can't* look after him!'

His heavily lashed grey-green eyes lifted to hers, holding them for a brief moment before returning to the baby lying in abandoned contentment in his arms.

'The point is, Jenny, that we're going to have to come up with something,' he said quietly. 'When it comes to the crunch, no matter how successful you or I may be at the work we do, we're neither of us indispensable— whereas, right now, your brother and my sister are... wouldn't you agree?'

'Of course I would,' she muttered uncomfortably.

'Their being part of a team geared to deal with precisely the type of catastrophe that's just happened in Czechoslovakia and being virtually on the spot is pretty miraculous...which is why Clare regards the fact that she's technically on a year's maternity leave as being neither here nor there.'

'Which is only natural—someone of her training finding herself in the middle of something as ghastly as that,' exclaimed Jenny with a decided twinge of guilt. 'Especially when she feels secure in the knowledge that my mother would be taking care of Jonathan. Jamie, what are we going to do?'

'I suppose we could tell Clare the truth...Graham would obviously stay on, but there would be nothing to stop her coming back—'

'How can you possibly say that?' exclaimed Jenny, aghast. 'It's specialists like Clare and Graham that the other doctors will be turning to for advice!'

'Well, she's ringing here in about half an hour,' he told her, returning the empty bottle to the tray and subjecting the baby to another bout of pummelling, 'so we'd better think up something to tell her.'

'Think up something?' repeated Jenny, her heart sinking somewhat. 'You make it sound as though you plan telling her a pack of lies!'

'Only a fool would try that,' he snapped with a flash of impatience that was a sharp reminder of how quick a temper he had. 'Right now, Graham and Clare are where they're most needed—desperately needed—and the last thing they deserve is worry over who's looking after their baby.'

'They're bound to worry when they realise Mum and Dad aren't around to do it,' protested Jenny.

'Why should they—there are the two of us, aren't there? Just let me finish, for heaven's sake!' he barked impatiently as Jenny shook her head vehemently. 'If I can be on the morning flight to Rio I could get back in time for you to be at work on time on Monday—Jenny, will you shut up and let me finish?' he roared as she began protesting volubly. 'And you can shut up too,' he growled softly to the baby at his shoulder who, far from being disturbed by his raised voice, was gurgling with delight. 'Jenny, all it necessitates is your having tomorrow off—on Monday you'll be back to work as usual.'

'Oh yes?' demanded Jenny furiously. 'How can you possibly get through trial runs in time to—?'

'I shan't be conducting the trials,' he cut in sharply. 'The rest of the team can handle those. The reason I *have* to get there by the weekend is that I've contracts to sign in connection with another boat, which are of great importance to my business. It's something I should have had tied up a couple of days ago and which I can't delay any longer, simply because those concerned only agreed to the signing taking place in Brazil in order to fit in with my schedule.'

'And what about the race you're entered in?' demanded Jenny heatedly. 'Presumably you intend returning to Brazil to participate in it—or can you navigate this new boat of yours by remote control?'

'If you'd let me finish,' he stated with steely softness, 'you'd hear that on Monday, when I get back, I intend lining up some trained nannies for us to interview—'

'Us?'

'Damn it, I can hardly interview them on my own!' he exploded. 'I've no idea what constitutes a good nanny.'

'And, being female, I have—is that it?'

'Forget it!' he snarled, rising to his feet. 'We'll just tell Clare the truth and let her sort it out for herself!'

'This is little short of emotional blackmail,' accused Jenny angrily, though even as she uttered the words she was conscious of her anger being directed more at herself than at the man towering over her and gazing down at her from chillingly impersonal eyes. 'Oh, for heaven's sake—this is ridiculous,' she groaned. 'Jamie, of course I'll do everything in my power to ensure Clare and Graham can get on with their work with complete peace of mind over Jonathan.'

'If that's the case, how is it you're so reluctant to hear what I have to suggest?' he demanded.

Jenny gazed up at him, tempted to ask him to sit down again, not because looking up at his well over six feet of height was giving her a crick in her neck—which it was—but for other, less specific, in fact, barely definable reasons. Towering over her was the man who, from the first instant she had become aware of the opposite sex, she had unquestioningly regarded as the embodiment of male physical perfection. Yet at some point during the past few years she had unconsciously become convinced that her previous perception of his looks had had far more to do with her juvenile obsession than with any fact. And now she wasn't in the least sure. For a reason she was unable to fathom, the sight of him standing there with one strong, darkly tanned arm supporting the baby against a broad shoulder seemed only to accentuate the extraordinary quality of his looks and the powerful, aggressively masculine magnetism he had always exuded.

'It's not that I'm reluctant to hear what you have to say,' she sighed, lowering her eyes as she fought to rid herself of those deeply unsettling thoughts. 'It's just that for a number of purely practical reasons this couldn't have happened at a worse time for me.'

To her relief he sat down again and began bouncing the baby on his lap.

'Shouldn't you try putting him in his cot?' she suggested uncomfortably, the complete unexpectedness of his actions triggering off the thought in her once more that none of this was really happening to her.

'He likes a bit of company after he's eaten,' he replied tersely, lifting the baby under the arms and letting him stand on his lap. 'Could you be a bit more explicit about these practical difficulties you're experiencing?' he added in that same tone. 'Clare will be ringing soon.'

'My main problem is that I have nowhere to live,' replied Jenny. 'I told you about the flat I missed out on. Actually, I was staying with Lizzie Street until I found somewhere—you remember Lizzie, don't you?'

He nodded impatiently, motioning her to continue.

'It was very kind of her to offer to put me up, but I can't possibly impose Jonathan on her as well.'

'You wouldn't have to—the most convenient solution for everyone is for you to stay at my place.'

He laughed as she started visibly.

'What's wrong, Jenny? Didn't you know I had a place in London...or is it the idea of sharing it with me that's the problem?'

'My only problem is that I know you far too well, Jamie Castile,' retorted Jenny, annoyed by the sensation of hot colour liberally washing her cheeks in response to the teasing mockery of his words.

'I doubt if you know me nearly as well as you believe; though, to be fair, my innate nobility of spirit can hardly have escaped you,' he murmured in drawling tones of mockery.

'Your innate nobility of spirit?' she drawled back, rolling her eyes heavenwards.

'Jenny, there can't be many healthily functioning males around into whose beds you've crept—nubile and devastatingly tempting—and left as pure as when you entered—'

'That's it!' raged Jenny, leaping angrily to her feet. 'I've had enough of you and your snide remarks—'

The two of them froze as the phone rang, the sound sending Jenny slumping back on to the seat from which she had just leapt.

'I suggest you answer it,' remarked Jamie coldly. 'After all, you're the one calling all the shots.'

Jenny levelled pleading eyes at him as the phone rang relentlessly on. His response was a dismissive shrug after which he turned his attention exclusively towards the baby trampling happily against his thighs.

Jenny snatched up the phone on the bedside table with no idea what she could possibly say.

'Hello—Clare?'

'Jenny! What a relief it is to hear your voice—I had

visions of Jamie trying to cope on his own with Jonathan until he got him to England,' exclaimed her sister-in-law.

'I'm sure he'd have managed,' said Jenny. 'How are things going where you are?' she added, the sound of Clare's voice making her suddenly acutely aware of the terrible devastation by which both she and Graham must be surrounded.

'I suppose we should all be thanking God that relatively so few were killed,' replied Clare, exhaustion tingeing her words. 'But one of the things for which Graham and I are specifically trained is to help the survivors cope with the horrific psychological trauma of it all. Jenny, you can't begin to imagine what it's like for these poor people. There are areas where entire villages have completely disappeared, some with virtually no loss of life...but it's almost akin to experiencing death for the inhabitants...they're huddled together, loath to leave the places where the majority of them have spent their entire lives, yet as they look around themselves they search in vain for a single landmark that can be recognised.'

'Clare, you sound utterly exhausted!' exclaimed Jenny anxiously.

'That's my own stupid fault,' claimed Clare. 'I'm afraid that what little opportunity I've had to sleep I've squandered worrying about Jonathan.'

'You probably won't like hearing this,' chuckled Jenny, 'but he doesn't appear to be missing either of you in the least.'

'That's why I realise how stupid I'm being,' admitted Clare sheepishly. 'Fortunately he's at the age where he'll go to anyone without a qualm...it's just that Jamie looked about as comfortable with him as a man with a time-bomb glued to his hands when they left.'

'Is that so?' laughed Jenny. 'Because right at this very moment your brother is sprawled across the bed and your son is bouncing with vigorous abandonment on him. Listen carefully and you might just be able to catch the racket accompanying each bounce.'

She held out the receiver just in time to catch a particularly piercing shriek of delight from the baby, to which his uncle responded with a theatrical groan.

'Your brat's just pulverised several of my ribs!' he bellowed accusingly in the direction of the receiver.

'I take it you heard all that,' murmured Jenny.

'All of it—loud and clear,' replied Clare, relieved laughter distorting her words. 'It's not that I even thought for one second he wouldn't be all right with Jamie—I think I got myself into a bit of a panic when I couldn't get through to your mother. How did she react to the news? I'm sure she's thrilled to bits at the idea of having him to herself for a while.'

Jenny's heart sank. 'She's going to be cursing fate when she finds out,' she began, forcing a humorous brightness into her tone. 'You see, she and Dad decided to take off for New Zealand slightly earlier than originally planned...so it's Auntie and Uncle who'll be having Jonathan all to themselves!'

'Oh God!' groaned Clare. 'This is terrible!'

'Terrible? Thanks a million!' exclaimed Jenny, with all the teasing indignation she could muster. 'Are you implying that Jamie and I aren't fit to look after him?'

Jamie sat up at those words, silently motioning her to bring the telephone to the bed.

'Jenny, this isn't a joking matter,' protested Clare as Jenny transferred herself and the telephone to the bed. 'You both have demanding jobs!'

'And we're both perfectly capable of organising our work schedules to accommodate our nephew,' stated

Jenny easily, starting slightly as Jamie pressed his face hard against hers in an attempt to hear what his sister was saying.

'I know that!' exclaimed Clare uncertainly. 'But it's far too much to ask of you both.'

'Clare, you and Graham are needed desperately right where you are,' said Jenny quietly. 'Of course it's not too much to ask of us. For heaven's sake, it's the least we can do!'

'And as for putting ourselves out,' butted in Jamie against the mouthpiece, while clasping the now dozing baby to him with one arm and slipping the other round Jenny for balance, 'on Monday we plan on setting about getting him a nanny who can take care of him during the day. How do you feel about that? I mean, we'll get someone highly qualified and vet her as no nanny has ever been vetted before.'

'Idiot,' laughed Clare. 'I know you would and I can't fault the excellence of your idea, but he'd disrupt your lives entirely—'

'Want to bet?' cut in Jamie with a chuckle. 'He's going to have to fit around us—starting from Monday, when the three of us are going disco dancing. Then on Tuesday—'

Jenny yanked the receiver closer to her own mouth. 'I've a feeling Jamie's trying to dispel your doubts,' she teased.

'Jenny, I haven't any doubts, but—'

'No buts, Clare,' stated Jenny firmly. 'Not only are you where you're most needed, but Jamie and I would probably never speak to you again if you turned our offer down.'

'OK, OK, he's all yours!' protested Clare with a groaned laugh. 'But if there's any chance of my taking a break and getting over to England, I'll grab it—just to check up that the pair of you aren't turning my son into a spoiled brat!'

'That's typical of my sister,' growled Jamie loudly in Jenny's ear. 'Doesn't the wretched woman realise we'll be the making of this child?'

'Of course she does,' chuckled Clare. 'But listen, folks, I'll have to go now—there's a queue forming for use of this telephone. Either Graham or I will ring you at Jamie's as soon as one of us can...and thanks a million, I really mean that and I hope you both appreciate how much.'

Jenny leaned over and replaced the receiver, the weight of Jamie's body—not to mention her sudden acute consciousness of it—rendering her movements awkward.

'What on earth are you doing?' she demanded sharply as the increasing pressure of his arm on her shoulders threatened to send her toppling.

'I'm trying to keep my balance,' he muttered in a strained voice. 'For heaven's sake, grab the baby, will you? My arm's completely asleep!'

Jenny eased the sleeping baby from him and placed him in the cot.

'Shouldn't we have changed his nappy?' she asked uncertainly as she straightened, a groan of laughter swiftly following her words.

'What's so funny?' he demanded, plainly not in the least amused as he rose, still rubbing his arm vigorously.

'You have to admit that there is something rather incongruous in the idea of anyone consulting you concerning a baby's welfare,' replied Jenny, more than a little nonplussed by the hostile look to which she was being subjected.

He shrugged, then made his way to the door, obviously not about to admit anything.

'He'd have soon let you know had he wanted his nappy changed,' he informed her brusquely, disappearing into the sitting-room. 'I'll get them to send up some coffee,' he called out. 'We might as well get all this thrashed out tonight, as I'll have to leave fairly early in the morning.'

Jenny followed him into the room, closing the bedroom door behind her. As he picked up the telephone extension and began ordering the coffee, Jenny spotted her overnight case, still sitting where the porter had left it. She frowned thoughtfully, wondering whether or not to offer to sleep in with Jonathan in the light of Jamie's proposed early start.

'You'd better sleep in with the kid,' he informed her as he replaced the receiver, his words managing to sound more like an order than a request. 'I'd like a night's sleep for a change.'

'There are a few things I'd like to make absolutely clear,' she stated coldly, almost beside herself with anger. 'I've agreed to get involved in this solely for Graham's and Clare's sakes. The give and take that will be necessary for this to work will in no way consist of my giving and your taking.'

As she spoke he began walking towards her, still flexing his left arm right up until the moment he drew to a halt scant inches from her.

'It really does still rankle, doesn't it, Jenny?' he taunted softly. 'The fact that you once offered me your all and I refused to take it.'

'I've no idea what you're talking about!' she spat, lashing out wildly at him and suddenly finding herself trapped in the circle of his arms.

'Liar,' he whispered, his head lowering to hers. 'I didn't even kiss you, did I, Jenny?' he murmured, his lips now hovering so close to hers that his every word seemed spoken on a shared breath. 'In fact, I've never kissed you...until now.'

It was a kiss that triggered off a half-remembered ache that swelled to painful sharpness within her beneath the hot incitement of the lips possessing hers. And, as the search of his mouth deepened in instant response to the hungry welcome of hers, her senses began leaping in tense expectancy, her body accepting with an uncharacteristically unquestioning fatalism its blatantly erotic response to every nuance of his. When she lifted her arms to encircle his neck it was almost as if she had felt compelled to move them in order to accommodate the hands that moved in seductive exploration to caress against her breasts. It was the alien sounds of her own soft moans of pleasure, wrung from her by the nerve-tingling search of those hands, that began resurrecting long-suppressed memories within her. It had been that inexplicable ache within her that had led her to this man's bed four long years ago; then blindly seeking a response from the lean masculine body which now was burning against hers with a blatancy of desire that was transforming the aching softness within her to an explosively demanding need.

But it was the ghostly echo of his taunting laughter that then drifted back to her across the years, reminding her of the implacable brutality with which he had once spurned her and returning her senses to her with a sharp cry of horror.

'It's all right—I'll get it,' he muttered hoarsely, confusing her completely with those inexplicable words as he released her and strode towards the door.

Her confusion lessened fractionally as she saw a waiter enter and move to the centre of the room to place a tray on a low oblong table.

She hadn't even heard the waiter's knock, she realised, watching the man retrace his steps while she remained as though transfixed to the spot. Yet Jamie had, and was obviously under the impression that it was the waiter's interruption that had elicited her cry of horror.

For several seconds after the door had closed behind the man, she remained where she was, striving to bring order to the erratic distortion of her breathing while at the same time bracing herself against the almost paralysing wave of humiliation flooding through her.

Then she turned, the pride he had once so brutally damaged rallying to her support in a sudden surge.

'Right, it's getting late—we'd better get down to business.' She moved swiftly towards a chair and sat down on it, willing herself not to give in to an almost ungovernable temptation to look around to find out exactly who it was who had uttered those briskly casual words.

Acutely conscious of his eyes on her, she trained her own on the hands clenched tightly on her lap, silently urging them to unclench. And even though she felt those eyes drilling into her, issuing their silent demands to be faced, her gaze remained locked on her hands.

'Jenny, you can avoid looking at me for as long as you like,' he taunted coldly. 'But it won't alter anything.'

'Really, Jamie, all we did was exchange a kiss,' she chided, inwardly stunned by the precise degree of disparaging amusement she had managed to inject into the words. 'And now that I've satisfied my curiosity, we really should get down to discussing Jonathan.'

'What the hell's that supposed to mean—now that you've satisfied your curiosity?' he demanded, his voice soft with barely suppressed rage.

'Oh for heaven's sake, Jamie!' she exclaimed lightly, part of her recoiling in horror, as she spoke, from this cool stranger now taking possession of her. 'I know I'm

a big girl now, but I really couldn't resist a sample kiss
from the man on whom I'd had such a colossal crush in
my teenage years!'

Her head rose in involuntary response to his sudden
movement, catching the chillingly murderous gleam in
his eyes as his hand reached out for the silver coffee-
pot on the tray. For one instant of stark fear she was
convinced he was about to pick it up and hurl it at her.

'Coffee?' he asked with an urbane detachment that
threw her completely, then began pouring without awaiting her reply.

It was when he passed her a cup that their eyes met,
the mocking challenge in his sending a premonitory
shiver of fear winging through her. It was as though
those shrewd grey-green eyes of his had the power to
pierce the veneer of hatred marring the wide-spaced blue
of the gaze they examined and to lay bare the helpless
uncertainty now gnawing within her.

CHAPTER TWO

AT ELEVEN o'clock on the following Monday night, Jenny dragged open the front door of Jamie Castile's luxury London flat in response to the sharp ring of the doorbell.

'My, what an unexpected surprise!' she hurled savagely at the visibly wilting figure of the man before her. 'What made you rush back like this? Don't tell me your precious boat sank on you!'

Flashing her a look of scowling dismissal, Jamie strode past her and into the parqueted hallway. Still not having offered her so much as a word of acknowledgement, he strode on and into the living-room—a huge, high-ceilinged room, sparsely yet exquisitely furnished in colours of the softest pastels.

Almost beside herself with outraged disbelief, Jenny flew in after him, the pressure of the fury building up in her since the early hours of the morning now barely containable as he silently flung his leather holdall on to an armchair and his tall, lean body face downwards and at full stretch on to the sofa.

'Six o'clock this morning—that's when you said your flight would touch down!' she almost screamed at his prone form as the travesty of her day flashed through her mind and demolished any remnant of control left in her. 'You haven't changed, have you? You're as thoroughly selfish and manipulative as you've always been!' she accused bitterly. 'I told you how much this job means to me. Heaven knows, I created a bad enough impression asking for time off before the start of an im-

portant campaign and after barely two weeks with the
company, so you can imagine how they must have felt
when I swanned in an hour late this morning and with
a baby in my shopping basket!'

His head rose from the cushion against which it had
been buried.

'You had the baby in a shopping basket?' he croaked,
his words as dazed as the expression on his face.

'What was I supposed to put him in?' she snarled.
'There aren't any pram shops on the way to where I
work; if there had been I'd have bought one...all I could
get was a large shopping basket.'

The breath she paused to take, on which she had intended to continue giving vent to her long-pent-up anger,
deteriorated into a gasp of fury as he began laughing
softly.

'How dare you—?'

'Give it a rest, for God's sake, Jenny,' he snapped, all
trace of laughter disappearing from him as he dragged
himself upright and began shrugging off his jacket.

'That's great—coming from you!' she shrieked, striding threateningly towards him, then halting, her eyes
widening in total confusion as he cast aside the jacket
and then began removing the silk shirt that had every
appearance of having been slept in. 'You've always used
others without any shred of compunction. Even as a
child, you had all the other kids in the village organised
into your own personal Mafia!' She broke off, frowning.
'What's that smell?' She leaned towards him and
sniffed. 'My God—you smell like a brewery!' she exclaimed in disgust.

'It's brandy,' he muttered, flinging his shirt aside then
leaning back and gazing up mockingly at her, the gleaming bronze of his naked torso rendered even darker by
the contrasting paleness of the upholstery.

Feeling somewhat overwhelmed—though uncertain whether it was caused by his casual admission or the disconcerting leap of her senses at the sight of such splendid near-nakedness—Jenny hesitated. Uncomfortably conscious of the suddenly loaded silence, she forced herself to look at him objectively. The last time she had seen him he had looked pretty exhausted—now he looked a positive wreck.

'My, my, Jenny—nothing to say?' he drawled.

'You're drunk!' she lashed out wildly, desperately trying to revive the momentum of her disconcertingly dying anger. Of course he was drunk, she told herself; a sober Jamie would at least have tried to charm his way into her good books, and doubtless given her a string of unconvincing excuses for his lateness…that was his way.

His eyes narrowed to dark slits as his broad shoulders rose and fell in a barely perceptible shrug. It was that slight movement that drew her attention to the ugly bruise staining down his right shoulder and disappearing into the dark profusion of hairs on his chest. And it was his raising of a hand to rub irritably against the dark stubble on his chin that brought a gasp from her. The knuckles of the hand, in fact, the entire back of it, was bruised and lacerated.

'You've been in a fight,' she accused in disgust.

He gazed down at his hand, then up at her, the smile creeping to his lips doing nothing to soften the brittle coldness glittering in his eyes.

'You know me so well, don't you, Jenny?' he murmured. 'In fact, there's no need for me to bother telling you what I've been up to—you've already worked it all out for yourself. Let's just check how far you've got. I'm drunk; I've been brawling—needless to say, over a woman—'

'Jamie, please! I…I—'

'You what, Jenny? Don't start going all coy on me. After all, it's common knowledge that I have an insatiable appetite for women.' As he uttered those ominously quiet words his eyes began travelling slowly down her body, openly stripping her. 'Talking of which,' he added softly, 'you're not the only one with a curiosity to be satisfied. Perhaps you'd care to continue where we left off a few years ago…only this time your presence in my bed will be greeted with unbridled enthusiasm—that I can guarantee.'

'You are completely despicable,' croaked Jenny, disconcerted to find herself fighting an urge to lash out at him physically.

'You sound almost surprised,' he murmured blandly. 'Which is odd, considering I still appear to be the selfish, manipulative tearaway you claim to know so well. Though there is one thing that puzzles me, Jenny,' he added innocently. 'With so little going for me—how is it that you managed to develop such an almighty crush on me?'

'What might have appealed to an adolescent is no longer material,' she informed him frigidly.

'Adolescent is the last word any sane person would have used to describe you the night I found you in my bed,' he retorted.

Wondering just how many more times he intended dragging up that ghastly incident, Jenny wisely bit back any retort; instead, she marched over to the armchair nearest her, removed his holdall from it and flung herself down.

'Tomorrow, when I return from work,' she announced tonelessly, 'I expect to find that you've arranged for suitable nannies to be interviewed. You'd also better get Jonathan a pram and a cot.'

'Where's he sleeping now?'

'He and I are in the spare room with the double bed,' she replied, her muscles aching in reminiscence of the struggle she had had dragging the heavy bed flush with a wall.

'Why didn't you take the room with the twin beds?' he asked. 'Hell, he's so tiny…aren't you scared of rolling over and squashing him?'

'I didn't put him in a single bed—simply because I was worried he might manage to roll out of it. And I shan't roll over and squash him…I've put a barricade of pillows between us,' she informed him wearily—and still she hadn't slept a wink for fear of something happening to the baby.

'Jenny, I honestly wouldn't have the first idea about how to go about buying a cot and a pram,' he protested.

'For heaven's sake, Jamie, you don't need a doctorate in one of the sciences to do it!' she exclaimed impatiently. 'Go to one of the big stores and ask for advice. I also think you should get a baby bath while you're at it.'

'He and I bathed together in Vienna,' muttered Jamie, suddenly stretching. 'He loved it.'

'I still think he should have his own bath,' insisted Jenny.

'Talking of baths,' he said, rising and stretching once more, 'I could do with a soak in one—care to join me?'

Jenny glanced up from the drawing-board as Ellie Brown entered the room. The tall, vivacious redhead was one of the company's top copywriters and also a friendly, refreshingly outspoken person. It was Ellie who had been the ringleader of the handful of staff—every one of them female—who had, the previous day, helped conceal Jonathan's presence from the eyes of those who would have objected.

'Gil Wardale says he'd like to see you when you have a spare minute,' announced Ellie, peering over Jenny's shoulder at her work. 'You really are very good, you know,' she murmured admiringly. 'Which is just as well, because rumour has it that Gil's got to hear of yesterday's cuddlesome addition to the staff.'

'Just my luck!' groaned Jenny, swinging round to face her. 'Something tells me my chances of surviving my trial period are just about nil,' she sighed gloomily.

'Now, now—let's not be so negative,' chided Ellie, then added with a sigh, 'but we might as well face the fact that Gil, with his tendency towards workaholism, won't exactly be thrilled to bits at the thought of his entire female staff having wasted the day clucking over a baby.'

'Whereas the truth is that most of them put in at least an hour's work,' quipped Jenny, her heart not in it in the least—she was worried sick.

Knowing she wouldn't have a moment's peace until she heard what Gil Wardale had to say, she made her way straight to his office after Ellie had left.

On her way it occurred to her that her present circumstances were making her examine certain aspects of her dream job a little more closely than she had previously. She had to admit that she had been more than a little in awe of the single-minded drive evident in Gil Wardale, a man probably no more than in his very early thirties and whose phenomenally successful company she had been so eager to join. Though now she also had to admit to herself that she had initially felt just the tiniest bit repelled by what could almost have been taken for fanaticism in his attitude to his work…yet she had quickly become infected by his forceful enthusiasm and had ended up regarding it as something to be admired. Now she wasn't quite so sure, she realised with a pang as she neared Gil Wardale's office. It was as though the world outside advertising didn't exist for him and the single-mindedly entrepreneurial men who comprised his management team, she thought, having difficulty putting her finger on exactly what it was that now struck her as being wrong. Throughout the country people were giving with unstinting generosity to collections in aid of the earthquake relief—yet she, and the other women who had helped secrete Jonathan, had seemed to know instinctively that the baby's connection with the disaster would have cut little ice with Gil Wardale and his associates.

There was no point trying to tug on heartstrings that didn't exist, accepted Jenny wryly as she knocked on the door.

'Be with you in a tick,' called out Gil Wardale to her, motioning her to be seated as he returned to his telephone conversation.

One of the first things that had struck her about this man was his clean-cut good looks, remembered Jenny as she took the seat before his desk. Almost as she had the thought, and to her intense irritation, a picture of Jamie flashed uninvited to her mind. OK, so he wasn't a patch on Jamie, she admitted irritably—how many men were? But the man before her was unquestionably attractive—he had strong, even features, and hair so unusually blond that it probably indicated Scandinavian ancestry and, though not tall, he was well-built and without a spare ounce of flesh on him.

Jenny gave a small shrug of understanding in answer to her employer's gesture of apology as his telephone conversation grew more prolonged; but she was experiencing a decided increase in the edgy feeling of tension besetting her. Yes—she was nervous about the negative impression she was bound to have made with her new company; but there was also Jamie to contend with. And she was finding it most disturbing that the image of his presence lurking in her mind seemed somehow almost dependable in its familiarity...which was absolutely ludicrous! The last person any member of her sex would be tempted to regard as dependable was Jamie Castile; dangerous and exciting, most definitely; but dependable—never in a million years!

'Sorry about that,' said Gil Wardale, cutting across her indignant thoughts, 'but that was one of our biggest clients,' he explained, then launched straight into discussing the campaign in which she was involved.

As his agile business mind moved swiftly from one pertinent point to the next, Jenny once again found herself slightly in awe of his total immersion in his work and the attention which he paid to even the most seemingly trivial of details. No wonder he had made such a name for himself, thought Jenny, feeling slightly shell-shocked after almost two hours of intense discussion.

'Well, you're managing to hang in there much as we expected you would,' he finally announced—a statement, Jenny gathered from his tone, that was intended as something of a compliment. 'Now, let's see what we can arrange,' he muttered, opening a desk diary beside him and leafing through its pages. 'I'm afraid Friday's about the only night I have free for some time—how about dinner?'

The words were so unexpected that Jenny had no chance to mask her surprise.

'Company policy,' he stated, the merest hint of amusement flickering in the wintry blue of his eyes. 'I like to make a point of wining and dining new team members—you know, get to know them one-to-one and fill them in on the company's little idiosyncrasies.'

'Oh...I see,' muttered Jenny, wishing she had managed to sound a little more businesslike: the truth was that for one uncomfortable moment she had actually thought he was asking her for a date! 'Yes—Friday would be fine.'

Once again she found Jamie's face leaping disconcertingly into her mind. It was just too bad if he had anything planned for that night, she told herself firmly— this was business, and, even had it not been, he was just going to have to get used to doing his fair share of babysitting. One thing was for sure: he would have no qualms about leaving her to do it when the occasion arose.

'Right,' stated Gil, snapping shut the diary and immediately reaching out as the telephone began ringing beside him.

Jenny found herself torn between remaining put and leaving as she listened to him speak. One of the things she liked least in this man—and in the other members of the top management staff—was a seeming inability to indulge in any conversation other than one related to work. To a man they seemed almost to 'switch off' once they had finished with the business they were discussing, as though rounding off their words with a few social pleasantries was an entirely alien concept to them.

Gil had obviously said all he wanted to say, Jenny decided, then rose to her feet and mimed a goodbye. It was the staying hand the man on the telephone raised towards her that returned her to her seat. A few moments later he terminated the call.

'One further point,' he rapped out. 'I believe you brought a child to the office yesterday.'

'Yes, I—'

'I don't remember any mention of your having a child during your interviews,' he interrupted coolly.

'He's not mine. He—'

'Glad to hear it. Apart from anything else, the presence of an infant would do nothing for the image we like to maintain within the company.'

'No, I'm sure it wouldn't,' agreed Jenny with acerbic quietness, her sense of justice outraged by his refusal to hear out her excuse. 'Though it won't happen again, I can assure you,' she added, surprised to find he appeared to have taken her agreement completely at face value.

'I'm sure it won't,' stated Gil, his smile as brisk and confident as his words. 'I'm a firm believer in tackling problems as and when they arise—it makes for better working relationships all round.' He leaned back against the soft black leather of the executive chair. 'And I've a feeling you will fit in and enjoy a very good working relationship with us, Jenny…I most certainly hope we shall.'

The sound of laughter drifted to Jenny's ears as she let herself into Jamie's flat that evening. She pulled a small face of discontent—she didn't feel in the least like socialising, especially not with one of the exotic creatures Jamie seemed to get entangled with, which the feminine lightness of the laughter warned her might well be the case.

'Jenny—in here!' his voice called to her. 'I've a surprise for you.'

She removed her jacket and walked into the sitting-room, experiencing a flash of irritation as her suspicions were confirmed. Seated on the sofa next to Jamie, and with a docile Jonathan on her knee, was a woman of exactly the type she had expected. Most of Jamie's women tended to be flawless creatures who looked as though they had stepped out of a fashion magazine—and this one wasn't exactly plain!

'I was just going to take a shower,' she announced vaguely, feeling thoroughly disgruntled.

'Bad day at the office, darling?' drawled Jamie, a remark that brought a flicker of surprise to the face of the woman next to him and an angry tensing in Jenny.

Deciding to ignore his remark, she gave the woman a half-hearted smile of greeting, then turned to leave.

'Jennifer!' Jamie's sharply censorious tone halted her. 'I'd like you to meet Mandy—our salvation.'

Jenny swung round. 'Our salvation?' she queried, not bothering to attempt hiding her puzzlement.

'Most definitely,' stated Jamie, bestowing a smile of supreme contentment on the woman now adjusting the baby on her knee in order to reach out a hand to Jenny—a hand which, for the sake of good manners, Jenny felt obliged to walk over and accept. 'Mandy's going to be looking after Jonathan as from tomorrow.'

'Really?' choked Jenny, the casual announcement knocking the breath from her.

'I'd better leave Jamie to explain,' exclaimed the woman with a small gasp of consternation as she looked at her watch. 'I'd no idea it was so late!'

Jamie solicitously took his nephew from her as she struggled to her feet, then rose to his own.

'Can I give you a lift anywhere?' he asked.

Mandy shook her head, an action, Jenny noted ill-humouredly, that seemed to interfere with her balance as she was forced to place a hand on Jamie's arm for support.

'I've got my own transport—but thanks for the offer,' murmured Mandy, smiling up at him. 'Sorry I've to dash like this, Jennifer, but I'll see you in the morning,' she added.

Jenny remained silent as she watched the curvaceous Mandy bid her farewell to the baby—an act which, to Jenny's increasingly acute perception, seemed to involve her almost burying her head, with its gleaming, shoulder-length cascade of hair almost the same colour as Jenny's own, against Jamie as she kissed the unprotesting infant. And as she watched man, woman and child leave the room she felt a murderous rage churning within her. How dared he? Did he honestly believe she would hand Jonathan into the so-called care of some dolly bird who happened to have caught his eye?

It was several moments before Jamie reappeared at the door, the baby still in his arms.

'I'll just put him in his pram,' he muttered, scowling across the room at her, then disappeared.

Well, at least he had managed to get a pram, Jenny told herself, a thought which did nothing to lessen the anger and indignation trembling within her as she marched off to her own room and began impatiently removing her clothes. There had actually been an element of accusation in that scowling look he had flung her—as though she were in some way at fault!

Trying to calm herself, she slipped into a housecoat and picked up her clothes. She needed a shower, she decided, if only to give her time to compose herself before confronting that…that…

'So this is where you're hiding,' observed Jamie, strolling into the room unannounced and right up to her. 'And what the hell was that about just now?' he demanded, gazing down at her from coldly assessing eyes.

'Get out of here!' she exploded, taking an involuntary step back from him and finding the backs of her legs trapped against the bed.

'Not until you've explained what that ill-mannered performance of yours was all about.'

'Ill-mannered! You've got a nerve!' she croaked indignantly. 'The agreement was that the *two* of us would interview any prospective nannies!'

'At the time, if I rightly remember, you were all for

my doing it alone,' he retorted, flinging himself down on the bed and gazing up at her accusingly.

'That's hardly the point,' hissed Jenny, glowering down at him. 'How do you imagine Clare's going to feel when she hears you've roped in one of your...your floozies to look after her child?'

'I've no idea,' he drawled, his eyes narrowing angrily as he propped himself up on his elbows.

'For God's sake, Jamie, don't you think it's about time you grew up and started taking life seriously?'

'Oh—now we're back to how irresponsible I am, are we?' he said, his tone ominously quiet. 'Exactly what is it that makes you think you have some God-given right to be my judge and jury, Jenny? I think it's time you were reminded of a few facts.'

'I don't need reminding of anything. All I—'

'You're eight years my junior—the kid sister of one of my closest friends. It probably seems to you that I've been around for as long as you can remember...but the fact is that you don't know me any more than I know you. You seem to be stuck in some sort of time-warp, repeating all the dire warnings the village biddies used to trot out when I was still a kid—'

'That's not fair!'

'No—it isn't,' he snapped. 'Yes, I was a tearaway as a kid, and yes, I have had possibly more than my fair share of women—but I can assure you, Jenny, not one of them is a floozie—'

'I'm sorry,' she cut in hastily, shame staining her cheeks. 'I had no right to say that...it's just that I feel so responsible for Jonathan.'

'And you think I don't?'

Jenny opened her mouth to protest, then clamped it firmly shut. There was no way she was going to allow herself to be manoeuvred into accepting Mandy as a

nanny, simply because she felt guilty over referring to
her as a floozie.

'Yes—well, that resounding silence manages to speak
volumes,' he noted sarcastically. 'The point that seems
to have escaped you—though mercifully not the rest of
the village dears—is that I am now a fully fledged adult
and perfectly able to take on the responsibilities that go
with that status, should the need arise.'

He rose from the bed and for an instant Jenny was
convinced he was about to stride from the room in disgust. Then he turned and grasped her without warning
by the shoulders.

'Tell me, Jenny, does it make you feel safer, kidding
yourself I'm still an irresponsible tearaway?' he asked
softly. 'Was I so irresponsible when I refused the very
considerable charms you once offered me?'

'I wondered how long it would be before you dragged
that up again!' she spat, struggling dementedly to free
herself.

'I keep referring to it because it was something of a
milestone in my life,' he replied, the tightening of his
arms rendering her struggles ineffectual. 'I readily admit
that twenty-seven is a little late to be reaching mental
maturity—but that was the night I finally grew up.'

'What's that supposed to mean?' she croaked, a tiny
part of her stalling against the seeming inevitability of
his kissing her while the rest of her tensed in breathless
expectation of it.

'It's supposed to mean that even irresponsible Jamie
had enough sense to realise that the consequences of
deflowering a nineteen-year-old ingénue might be more
than he could handle.'

'You wouldn't have been deflowering me—as you so
gallantly put it!' she lied, goaded by a sense of helpless
outrage.

'I can assure you I'd not have been so damned gallant had I known you were experienced at the time,' he muttered, drawing back slightly from her with a rueful laugh. 'I used up more self-control that night than I ever knew I possessed.'

Jenny felt her pulse-rate shift into a higher, almost painful gear. 'Now you really are being gallant,' she managed and was appalled to hear a note of wistfulness in her slightly breathless words. 'You swatted me aside with about as much thought as you'd have given to an irritating fly.'

'If you say so,' he stated in oddly clipped tones, pulling her heavily against him. 'Who am I to argue with someone who knows me as thoroughly as you do? And who cares anyway?'

There was a heated turbulence in his kiss that contrasted oddly with the cool carelessness of his words; and, as that heat permeated and possessed her, she felt its swift destruction of those self-protective layers built up so painstakingly over the years.

Yet, even as her lips and body were responding with eager spontaneity to the urgent surge of passion in his, she was unable to silence the doom-laden voice within her warning that she was as besotted with this infuriatingly exciting man now as she had ever been.

CHAPTER THREE

JAMIE'S initial reaction was that he thought Jenny was joking—a joke he found it impossible to share, judging by the sudden wariness diluting the soft somnolence of passion in his eyes. Then he drew back from her, wariness hardening to disbelief as he gazed down at her sprawled beneath him on the bed.

'"No" is what you should have been saying a good five minutes ago—not now,' he rasped, rolling away from her and dragging himself upright. 'And, to be brutally frank, some men would regard themselves justified in considering you to have been cutting it dangerously fine even five minutes ago.'

As he rose from the bed Jenny drew the gaping robe back over her exposed breasts, her badly shaking hands an indication of an inner turmoil that made speech impossible. She sat up, hugging her arms to her in a desperate attempt to rid herself of the still tingling imprint of his hands on her body and the intoxicating heat of him still burning along the length of her. And, as the terrible hunger raged on unabated within her, she found herself dazedly trying to recall what words she had used in that barely conscious moment when she had acted contrary to her every desire and had denied both herself and him.

'Jamie—where are you going?' she protested automatically as, with an exclamation of disgust, he turned from her and strode from the room.

'This is all I need!' she wailed softly to herself, clutching her head as though willing it to start functioning once more.

When her head eventually obliged, it was to present her with the observation that the only way peace could be restored to her life would be for Jamie to be out of it entirely—a comfortless observation, given the presence of Jonathan in their lives.

But she certainly couldn't leave things hanging in the air as they now were, she told herself dejectedly, rising from the bed and making her way to the sitting-room.

He was pouring himself a drink as she entered.

'Jamie—I'd like to apologise,' she began, then broke off, distracted by the fact that his hands, pouring the drink, were no more steady than her own. 'I...you took me completely by surprise,' she added disjointedly and silently cursed herself for not having had the wits to have worked out what she was going to say to him.

Without even casting a glance in her direction, he moved to one of the armchairs and sat down, sprawling untidily on it as he gazed moodily into his glass.

'What you actually mean is that you took yourself by surprise,' he retorted sharply, cold speculation in his eyes as they rose to hers. 'Which mucked up your plans for revenge somewhat.'

'Revenge?' croaked Jenny.

'Wasn't that your intention—to string me along and then give me a taste of what you considered to be my own medicine?' he enquired frigidly. 'Too bad your body put up such a struggle against co-operating with your vengeful little mind.'

'For heaven's sake, Jamie—what are you saying? How could you possibly think I'd stoop that low?'

'How indeed?' he muttered eventually, plainly a little thrown by the sincerity of her indignation. 'OK—perhaps you'd care to explain yourself,' he added harshly, returning to his morose contemplation of the contents of his glass.

Jenny walked over to the chair opposite his and sat down gingerly on its edge, wondering what on earth she could possibly say. The truth was something she had yet to examine, she thought frantically; and even if she had, the chances were it was the last thing she would ever want to confide in Jamie.

'Hell, you almost had me convinced I was wrong in thinking your motive was revenge!' he exploded through her panicking thoughts.

'You *were* wrong,' she shrieked back at him. 'It's just that...that I—'

'Why the hell did you let things get so nearly out of hand?' he ripped through her stammered words. 'Even a woman with absolutely no experience whatever with men would think twice before behaving in so dangerously provocative a way and then calling a halt to the proceedings!'

'Jamie, I...' She broke off with a groan of total frustration as her mind went a complete blank...all she needed was one convincing lie, before she curled up and died of humiliation! 'I...I had no right to let myself become so carried away like that with you...not when there's another man in my life.'

As she sank back in her chair, almost weak with relief, she saw Jamie glance up from his drink, his eyes noticeably widening. Then, to her total confusion, he began chuckling softly to himself.

'So—Jenny doesn't go in for two-timing, is that it?'

'Of course I don't!' she exclaimed indignantly, the hot colour then flooding her cheeks nothing to do with indignation but everything to do with her sudden realisation that her hitherto inexplicable inability to sustain any romantic relationships with men might have a lot to do with some subconscious and altogether ridiculous wish to remain faithful to this particular man—one who had probably not given her even so much as a passing thought during the past four years!

'So, ditch him.'

'I beg your pardon,' she croaked.

'Jenny, you want me every bit as much as I want you,' he pointed out, in tones she found disconcertingly dispassionate, given the subject. 'So the obvious solution is to ditch him before you're unfaithful to him by deed as well as—'

'I've no intention of either ditching him—as you put it—or of being unfaithful to him,' she butted in sharply, appalled by the startlingly sensuous effect his words were having on her. 'In fact, I was going to ask you to keep Friday free for baby-sitting Jonathan—he and I have a dinner date.'

'Too bad—I could be away on business then.'

Jenny opened her mouth to protest that hers too would be a business engagement and only just managed to bite back the words.

'So I suggest you ask Mandy if she can stay late.'

'Jamie, you talk as though it's a foregone conclusion I'll agree to Mandy looking after Jonathan,' she stated icily.

'And why shouldn't it be?' he enquired.

'Because you just can't employ *anybody* for something as important as that!' she protested exasperatedly. 'For instance, what sort of qualifications does the woman possess? Or does she possess any, apart from looks?'

'Now, now, Jennifer,' he murmured. 'Your jealous streak is showing.'

And jealousy was precisely what she felt, she realised, her stomach lurching sickeningly.

'You always have to reduce things to your totally irresponsible level,' she accused, more furious with herself than with him. 'I suggest—'

'And I suggest you stop droning on about my irresponsibility and listen to a few facts,' he cut in harshly. 'We're hiring Mandy simply because that's what Graham and Clare want.'

'Graham and Clare?' demanded Jenny, openly sceptical.

'Graham rang this afternoon—'

'Why on earth didn't you tell me?'

'I'm trying to tell you now, damn it!' he snarled. 'From whatever grapevine that's working among the medical team out there, he and Clare got to hear that Mandy might be free—apparently she used to work for friends of theirs. Anyway, they managed to contact her and luckily she is free.'

'Why couldn't you have told me all this in the first place?' demanded Jenny, suddenly feeling utterly mortified.

'What—and miss the delightful spectacle of you fuming with jealousy?' he chuckled.

'You really do regard yourself as God's gift to women,' she retorted as witheringly as she possibly could, given the fact that her cheeks had flared to a violent hue.

'A delusion I might well have been under had I not been convinced otherwise by too many women to ignore,' he replied with another chuckle, then rose, flashing her a teasing grin as he walked past her and out of the room.

Jenny leaned back her head and closed her eyes, a feeling she could only describe as one of total defeat washing over her. She was almost twenty-four, for heaven's sake, she remonstrated dejectedly with herself; yet at this very moment she felt no less confused and uncertain than she had at sixteen. She had spent the past four years in what amounted to a virtual emotional limbo—trying to cure herself of her infatuation with a man who was inordinately fascinating, even by standards far more sophisticated than hers. And for probably as much as two of those years she had managed to convince herself she had succeeded, simply by using that palpably dangerous expedient of never allowing him to enter her thoughts. And now what?

'Don't tell me you've dozed off!'

Jenny let out a yelp of shock as she heard those softly teasing words and felt her head tilted backwards between strong hands.

'For heaven's sake, Jamie—you're making my head swim!' she protested irritably as she gazed up at his laughing upside-down face.

'I'll be doing more than just making your head swim, that I promise you, Jenny,' he chuckled, his mouth lowering to hers in a lazy, lingering and altogether mind-blowingly intoxicating kiss. 'Just as soon as you ditch Friday's date,' he murmured huskily against her parted lips.

Jenny gazed surreptitiously across the table at her dinner companion as the waiter served them both coffee, finding herself in the puzzling position of being uncertain as to whether or not she was enjoying his company. That Gil Wardale had turned out to possess an unexpectedly wry sense of humour was a decided bonus in the evening she had been positively dreading. But he was disconcerting company too, in that twice during the evening she had found herself unable to decide whether he had been flirting with her; whether he had or not was neither here nor there—it was her genuine inability to read him that disturbed her in that it left her feeling inexplicably gauche and vulnerable.

'How does working in London compare to Brighton?' he asked suddenly, his first words during the evening that were even remotely personal. 'You were with a firm in Brighton before joining us, weren't you?'

Jenny nodded. 'It's quite a bit different,' she admitted. 'But then, Wardale's is in a completely different league from my old firm.'

'Which, as you say, no doubt accounts for the difference,' agreed Gil, a slight hint of wryness in his smile. 'And what about living in London?' he asked. 'It must seem all concrete and grimness after the Sussex countryside—even though the area you're in is certainly very up-market.'

Despite a strong suspicion that she was being probed as to her material background, Jenny laughed good-humouredly. He must have assumed she was renting, or had even bought, one of the flats outside which she had arranged to meet him...no wonder he was curious as to her background!

'It certainly is,' she smiled. 'But I couldn't afford somewhere like that in a month of Sundays—not even on the very good salary you're paying me,' she added hastily, then hesitated, tempted to try explaining about Jonathan once more and then deciding against it: he had shown no interest then, so why should he suddenly now? 'I...I'm sharing with friends until I find somewhere of my own.'

'You're fortunate to have friends able to give you such a pleasant introduction to living in London,' observed Gil.

'Yes, and I dare say I'm in for quite a shock when I start looking at places I can actually afford,' she sighed.

'That's one of the drawbacks with London,' murmured Gil, leaning back slightly on his chair and gazing across at her from those disconcertingly cold blue eyes of his, 'the astronomical rent charged for next to nothing.' He smiled suddenly, a bright, almost boyish smile. 'Are you in any particular rush to find somewhere?'

Jenny hesitated; she actually had no idea how long she and Jamie would be looking after Jonathan, though even as she shook her head she realised it would probably be a wise move to start looking around fairly soon.

'That being the case, I suggest you leave it with me for a while—one thing I do have is contacts and there are one or two bargains around to be had.'

'That's very kind of you,' said Jenny, and meant it sincerely. 'But I'm not thinking of buying a place.'

'I didn't necessarily think you were,' replied Gil. 'There are quite a few very decent properties available on what might be termed a caretaking basis—where the owners wouldn't put them on the open market for fear of getting the wrong sort of tenant.'

'But surely that sort of thing would be rather short-term,' said Jenny dubiously.

'Not all of them,' countered Gil with a smile. 'And, as you're in no rush, I'd be quite happy to put a few feelers out...if you have no objections.'

'Objections?' gasped Jenny, laughing. 'I'd be extremely grateful—finding somewhere to live is something I've not been looking forward to in the least!' she added, his completely unsolicited generosity awakening feelings of remorse in her for having judged him to be no more than a hard-bitten businessman and a rather cold fish.

'I'm glad I thought to mention it to you,' he murmured, then suddenly gave another of those wry smiles she was beginning to find rather attractive. 'And I'm glad, too, that I've managed to persuade you there's also

another side to the workaholic advertising man...though
don't ever bank on seeing it during working hours.'

Jenny was still trying to puzzle out exactly what to make
of Gil Wardale when she let herself into Jamie's flat and
decided she was probably asking the impossible so soon.

'Mandy?' she called out in alarm, as Jonathan's lusty
roars greeted her ears.

It was Jamie who appeared in the doorway of the sitting-room, dressed only in the bottom half of a pair of
navy silk pyjamas and with the yelling baby in his arms.

'Where's Mandy?' she gasped.

'I sent her home when I arrived, and anyway, it's long
past midnight—or hadn't you noticed?'

'What's wrong with Jonathan?' she demanded, ignoring the open accusation in his tone.

'Temper—I've just made a feed up for him and he's
too greedy to wait for it to cool down.'

A situation which wouldn't have arisen if he had made
the feed up in advance, thought Jenny indignantly—no
doubt he had been expecting her to be around to do it.

'Have you tried standing it in cold water?' she yelled
over the baby's increasing wails, and was immediately
treated to a withering look.

'Perhaps you'd care to check if it's cooled sufficiently,' he roared over his shoulder to her as he turned
and ambled back into the sitting-room.

Jenny went to the kitchen and tested the bottle standing in a jug of what had originally been cold water—it
was still far too hot. She emptied the jug of its now
warm water, replacing it with cold, then sat down at the
kitchen table and gazed morosely into space.

She had walked into the flat, her mind preoccupied
with Gil—and then Jamie had appeared and that churning, aching need that had taken to erupting in her without

warning had started up with a vengeance. Whatever these feelings she had for him, she needed them like a hole in the head and she had better start doing something to rid herself of them pretty quickly—before she ended up a nervous wreck.

She reached over and tested the milk once more, deciding to give it another few seconds. A few weeks ago she had started a job that had filled her with a sense of purpose and achievement, she reflected bitterly, and now she was even beginning to regard that with a slightly jaundiced eye.

Feeling, if anything, more confused and dejected than ever, she picked up the bottle and took it into the sitting-room.

'Would you like me to give it to him?' she offered, then promptly handed Jamie the bottle without awaiting a reply as the baby's grizzles turned once more to full-throated bellows.

'Talk about a deafening silence,' chuckled Jamie, as his charge began guzzling contentedly. 'You wouldn't believe anything so tiny could make such an almighty din.'

Jenny sat down, her heart sinking into further dejection as her eyes took in the picture of the half-clad man nonchalantly feeding the baby. She was remembering the first sight she had had of him in Vienna and once again she found herself puzzling over the seeming paradox of the almost aggressive masculinity he still managed to exude despite the totally unmasculine task he was performing.

'Well—how did he take it?'

Jenny started slightly, shaking herself free from her thoughts. 'How did who take what?'

'Lover-boy being ditched. Surely you...' He broke off

with a startled look as the telephone rang, then gave a soft chuckle. 'Talk of the devil, perhaps?'

'My friends have more manners than to ring at this hour,' she informed him haughtily, confident that none of her friends had this number as she stretched over towards the small onyx table on which the telephone sat. 'It's for you,' she then informed him smugly, leaping up to take the baby from him.

And, needless to say, it was a woman, she added silently to herself as she settled the now cherubic baby in her arms and continued feeding him.

'Ginny—hi! You'll have to speak up, the line's terrible,' yelled Jamie into the receiver as he threw himself down on the chair Jenny had just vacated. 'Where's Mark? And the trials…? No problem—I'll be back in Rio in a few days anyway.'

And only for as long as it took for him to participate in the race, Jenny vowed to herself, removing the emptied bottle from the baby and lifting him on to her shoulder; because, once the final details of the campaign had been thrashed out, she might well be saying goodbye to routine working hours.

'So that's the reason behind this call,' chuckled Jamie. 'I warned Juanita not to tell you…no, I'm fine, I promise…no, I had to get a later plane.'

Jenny felt her ears prick instantly, not that they actually had to; the way he was bellowing down the receiver there was no conceivable way she could avoid hearing what he was saying.

'I know that's what they thought at the hospital, but believe me, it was less a case of concussion than all the brandy some well-meaning idiot poured down my throat before the ambulance arrived—not to mention over me! Tell Juanita I owe her a new car—hers must have just about been written off.'

And she had as good as accused him of drunken brawling, thought Jenny weakly, pressing her burning cheek against the now-sleeping bundle at her shoulder as she remembered the night he had arrived...and he had simply egged her on.

He was still on the phone when she rose and took the baby to his room.

'Are you going to be a good boy and sleep right through again?' she whispered to her oblivious nephew, tucking him into the cot now standing between the two single beds in the spacious room and then walking over to the window.

First the misunderstanding over Mandy and now this, she thought defeatedly as she let her forehead drop against the welcome coldness of the window pane. And both times she had automatically leapt to the worst conclusion possible...not that he had exactly gone out of his way, on either occasion, to provide her with the truth.

'Is he asleep?'

She turned as he spoke and walked from the window.

'Yes,' she replied, closing the door behind her as she joined him in the hall. 'Jamie, why did you allow me to think all those terrible things about you?' she demanded woodenly.

'I wasn't aware I possessed any powers of veto over your thoughts,' he drawled sarcastically. 'Though I have to admit to finding a little intriguing some of those thoughts you do have concerning me.'

'You would,' she retorted, his scathing tone igniting a sudden anger in her that stripped her of all guilt as she turned towards her own room.

'And what's that supposed to mean?' he demanded, catching her by the arm and swinging her round to face him. 'Jenny, why can't you just...? Oh hell!' With a soft groan he pulled her to him. 'Jenny,' he whispered, her

name catching like a soft growl in the back of his throat
in the instant before his lips began a wild, intoxicating
bombardment of hers.

A feeling close to desperation driving her, she clung
to him, her response to the bruising urgency of his mouth
uninhibitedly inviting.

'We've wasted so much time,' he protested barely co-
herently, slumping back heavily against the wall as his
arms half lifted her against him.

There was impatience in the hands that slid beneath
the fine wool of her sweater to explore against her skin
then swiftly rise to undo the catch on her bra. And, with
no need of urging from him, it was she who automatically raised her arms to accommodate his removal of
both garments.

'You're beautiful...so beautiful,' he breathed huskily,
green glittering like emeralds in the darkness of his eyes
as he lowered his head to the curve of her throat.

She felt every nerve in her body leap in agonising
response to the abrasive coolness of his touch against
her flesh, a soft cry exploding from her as her own hands
reached out to him, trembling and hesitant as they hovered indecisively.

'I'm the only man you have room for in your life right
now,' he whispered, lifting her arms around him, then
drawing her back against him.

She felt the silky abrasiveness of his chest hairs momentarily against her skin, then he lowered his face to
her breasts, his exploring mouth against their straining
tautness sending sharp jolts of desire ripping through her
despite the frantic racing of her mind to digest his words.

Right now, her beleaguered mind shrieked at her, even
as her arms clung around his head to imprison him
against her. Right now there could be no room in her
life for any man bar him...but what about later? There

had never been—never would be—room for any man
but him.

'Jamie,' she pleaded hoarsely, his name spilling from
her as the moist search of his mouth against her flesh
threatened to drug her mind to a standstill.

He lifted his head from her, his body straightening
once more as he drew her slightly from him to gaze
down at her from eyes dark with the somnolence of desire. And again she was fighting the drug-like effect of
her own desires as they threatened to silence her reason.

'Jamie, I…what about the other women in your life?'
she choked, at the last minute balking at facing up to
her real fears.

'They're not important,' he murmured with husky dis-
missiveness, his hands impatient as they drew her fully
against him once more, moulding her still trembling
body to the uninhibited desire in his.

'But they exist,' she persisted, her mind battling dog-
gedly on, even as her body threatened to melt in blatant
acquiescence to his.

She sensed an almost imperceptible tensing within
him.

'It's not the same…my relationships probably involve
a lot less commitment than yours do.'

'Oh—I see. And, despite your own lack of commitment, you feel you have every right to demand my ex-
clusive attention, while you—'

'If you want me to put all other relationships on ice,
why not just say so?' he parried warily.

Jenny found herself turning the phrase 'on ice' over
in her mind, feeling rather as though she had just had a
bucketful of it tipped over her. *Right now*—as in 'just
for the time being'—he wanted no other men in her life,
she told herself calmly, and, just in case she hadn't got
the message, he had magnanimously offered to put his

other relationships *on ice*—as in 'there to be revived
once his fling with her was over'!

'That's terribly sweet of you, Jamie,' she managed
evenly, stifled outrage sparing her even the slightest
twinge of humiliation as she drew back from his unre-
sisting arms. 'But you needn't go to all that trouble.'

'Jenny...hell, I've obviously said the wrong thing!'
he exclaimed edgily. 'I—'

'How could there possibly be anything wrong in your
speaking the truth?' she enquired lightly, a faint glimmer
of satisfaction piercing the terrible calm within her holding rage at bay as she glimpsed a sudden uncertainty in
his expression. 'You see, we're more alike than you
seem to realise,' she continued, driven to score every
point she could before the unnatural calm deserted her
and she was left with nothing but total humiliation. 'My
involvements with men are no more committed than
yours are with women, so naturally I had no intention
of ending my relationship with...with Gil.' She hesitated
only fractionally before inserting her boss's name into
her tissue of self-preserving lies, then took another
breath on which to continue—only to have it expelled
from her almost before it had had a chance to reach her
lungs as she was grasped by the arms and lifted half off
her feet.

'Are you telling me you went out with him tonight
with no intention of giving him his marching orders?'
roared Jamie.

'That's *exactly* what I'm telling you,' retorted Jenny,
so thrown by his undisguised fury that she barely noticed
the calm slipping from her.

'I thought you didn't go in for two-timing,' he accused
harshly, releasing her so suddenly that her legs almost
gave way beneath her.

'I don't—normally!' she retorted, rage now gaining

an almost total hold on her in the face of the arrogant blatancy of his double standards. 'But, you being you, it hardly seemed to matter.'

The instant she had finished uttering the words, she realised she had gone too far, and for one split-second she actually thought he was about to hit her before he pushed her angrily away from him.

'God almighty, I don't believe I'm hearing this!' he exploded savagely. 'How did you plan accommodating us both—night shifts in strict rotation?'

For an instant she stared at him blankly, then she heard her own sharp intake of breath as the meaning of his accusing words dawned on her. She had begun lying off the top of her head the other night, simply out of pride, and had continued doing so tonight with a reckless abandon…she hadn't even considered possible repercussions, least of all that he would assume she was sleeping with this fictitious other man!

She refilled her lungs, dragging nervous fingers through her hair as she read the glittering condemnation in his eyes.

'I'm surprised a man with your reputation with women can't stomach a bit of competition!' she hurled at him defiantly—how dared he look at her like that?

'So you *are* sleeping with him!'

'It's none of your damned business what I'm doing with him!' she shrieked, beside herself with rage.

His eyes widened in shock, then swiftly narrowed to coldness as they slowly raked her nakedness.

Jenny stood before him, conscious of what he was trying to do to her and clenching her arms rigidly to her sides rather than admit defeat by raising them to cover herself. And she defiantly stood her ground even when he took a step towards her, then reached out and cupped her face in his hands.

'It seems we've reached a temporary stalemate,' he muttered softly. 'But in the end someone will have to give in—I wonder which of us it will be.'

'I don't know what you mean,' she said hoarsely, every nerve in her body crying out for his touch.

'It's quite simple, really,' he murmured, his hands sliding from her face to her shoulders in slow caress. 'You want me on your terms—I want you on mine...the only certainty is that only one of us can win.'

There was only the slightest of pressure from his hands as he drew her slowly towards him, so little that it would have been the easiest thing in the world for her to slip free and then walk away. She did neither, and, when their bodies finally met, the swift jolt of tension jarring through them brought a hoarse groan of protest from him.

'Of course, if it weren't for my legendary pig-headed stubbornness, I'd say this is one battle I had no chance in hell of winning,' he muttered with a groaned laugh, suddenly hugging her to him fiercely before releasing her and walking away without once looking back.

CHAPTER FOUR

ELLIE BROWN scrawled a few hieroglyphics across the last of the proofs and added it to a large pile of others.

'Thank God that's over and done with!' she exclaimed. 'To be perfectly frank, I thought one of us would crack long before we were through that lot, because you, Jennifer Page, look almost as bad as I feel.'

Jenny leaned back in her chair and gazed at the pile of proofs, the sight of which earlier had led her to wonder where all her initial enthusiasm for her job had gone.

'I hope sincerely you don't feel *that* bad,' she muttered, bringing a startled glance from Ellie as the humour she had intended injecting into her words failed to appear.

'You should be thanking your lucky stars it's only a baby—and not even your own—that you're losing sleep over,' sighed Ellie glumly. 'Mine's the fully developed version—male, needless to say.'

'Actually, Jonathan's been a perfect angel for the past few nights,' said Jenny, almost with a touch of pride, then immediately raked her fingers through her hair in a gesture of embarrassment as she realised what she had said.

'Don't tell me your problem's fully grown too,' groaned Ellie and, much to Jenny's relief, launched into a decidedly uncharacteristically disjointed summary of what was troubling her.

'You're losing sleep over the fact that he wants to marry you?' queried Jenny, puzzled.

Ellie gave an embarrassed shrug. 'I know I sound like

61

a raving nutcase,' she muttered uncomfortably. 'But I honestly wasn't aware there was a man of my dreams until Peter walked into my life and now...now I'm just terrified it all really is a dream and one of these days I'm going to wake up.'

'Oh, Ellie, you really are a raving nutcase,' chided Jenny softly.

'My mother's getting so fed up with me that she suggested to Peter that we elope and put everybody out of their misery.' She gave an almost evil-sounding chuckle. 'Can you imagine how Gil and his henchmen would react if I upped and eloped in the middle of a campaign? It doesn't bear thinking of!'

Their laughter was interrupted by the ringing of the telephone.

'Jenny—Gil Wardale here,' came the terse words in her ear. 'About that conversation we had regarding your accommodation—are you still interested?'

'Yes—I am.'

'A couple of possibilities might be coming up shortly—both on virtually a caretaking basis, with whoever goes in paying only a nominal rent.'

'That sounds fantastic.'

'Obviously I can't promise anything, but I'll chase both up and let you know if either materialises.'

'That's very kind of you—thank you, Gil,' said Jenny, feeling inexplicably touched as she replaced the receiver.

'He's a funny old character, is our Gil,' sighed Ellie, when Jenny had explained. 'A real slave-driver most of the time and secretive as hell about his personal life—I sometimes wonder if he actually has a life outside these walls—but underneath that concrete exterior there definitely lurks a soft-hearted centre!' She gave a sudden chuckle. 'I meant to ask you how the statutory meal went the other night—I suppose you couldn't quite make up your mind whether or not he was trying to flirt with you.'

Jenny laughed as she nodded.

'Don't worry, those of us who have been subjected to it have come to the conclusion he's convinced it's a requirement that goes with entertaining females—not that he'd ever dream of getting romantically involved with an employee,' laughed Ellie, then suddenly grew serious. 'He's not nearly as confident in relationships as he is in business...and, it being business, I suppose he had no problem warning you that Jonathan wasn't to darken these doors again.'

'Yes, and he won't, thank heavens—we've got him a nanny.'

'We?' enquired Ellie.

'My brother-in-law and I are looking after him jointly,' explained Jenny. 'Though I'm not sure if that's what he is, technically,' she added uncomfortably. 'But "my brother's wife's brother" is a bit of a mouthful.'

'It certainly is,' chuckled Ellie. 'Is he by any chance the one you're losing sleep over?' she asked, then immediately began apologising. 'I'm sorry, Jenny, that was unforgivably nosy.'

'Oh, it's nothing like that!' exclaimed Jenny hastily, and was annoyed to find herself feeling virtually as if she had lied. 'I've known Jamie since I was a child—and there are times when he can be an absolute pain in the neck,' she added with a forcefulness that did nothing to alleviate that vague feeling of guilt.

'I get it,' murmured Ellie sympathetically. 'Your joint responsibility consists of you doing all the work.'

Jenny now felt positive guilt as she nodded; Jamie had, in fact, proved surprisingly capable of doing his bit, even though it took constant nagging on her part to get him to tackle anything he didn't particularly relish.

'Just you make sure he doesn't get away with it,' advised Ellie, glancing down at her watch and then rising. 'And now it's high time we put this lot away and went home.'

Jenny made her way home completely lost in thought. At one point she startled herself by laughing out loud as she tried to imagine Ellie's reaction to the ridiculous corner into which she had managed to manoeuvre herself—where her only way out, according to her own admittedly confused assessment of the situation, was to seduce Jamie! Then she was remonstrating angrily with herself that it wasn't in the least funny. Almost from the moment she had walked through the door of that hotel suite in Vienna, her life had been reduced to complete chaos and what was more—

'Jenny, hi! We were wondering where you'd got to!'

At the sound of Mandy's cheery and unreservedly welcoming words, Jenny's eyes rose to focus several yards ahead of her, to where Mandy and Jamie were descending the steps from the flats.

'Isn't he adorable?' laughed Mandy, snuggling up to Jamie.

Jenny froze to a halt. It wasn't so much that those words and that clinging, almost fawning behaviour seemed utterly incomprehensible to her, coming from someone as level-headed and extremely likeable as she now knew Mandy to be; it was more that her gut reaction was to race towards the two of them and hurl them apart. It was a reaction so savage in its immediacy that, when it eventually began subsiding in her, she found herself frantically trying to convince herself her memory of it was exaggerated...even imagined.

'Jenny?' called out Jamie, making no attempt whatever to escape Mandy's clutches, noted Jenny sourly.

'Hello,' she muttered, now switching to telling herself

her reaction had merely been one of irritation at the sight of two adults indulging in such childish canoodling in public.

She began urging her reluctant feet forward and it was as she took her first hesitant step that Mandy made a soft gurgling noise and leaned her gleaming auburn head so far into Jamie's half-zipped leather jacket that it almost disappeared from sight…and it was in that instant that Jenny saw red.

'Are you two out of your minds?' she demanded, now striding purposefully towards them. 'How dare you leave Jonathan unattended…?' Her words gasped to a halt as Jamie turned fully towards her and she caught sight of the baby nestling inside his jacket.

'You were saying?' he drawled, his face tense with anger.

Scarcely able to believe the gross distortions her imagination had managed to present her with in those few moments, Jenny turned to gaze into Mandy's shocked face with an expression of abject apology.

'I'm sorry—I really should have given you more credit than that,' she exclaimed hoarsely. What on earth had possessed her?

'Not to worry,' replied Mandy, her eyes puzzled. 'You're bound to feel over-protective towards Jonathan, under the circumstances. But you can rest assured, I'd never dream of leaving him alone.'

'Mandy…I don't know what came over me. I'm so sorry!'

'And so you damned well should be,' snapped Jamie.

'No—Jenny's right,' protested Mandy, plainly not one to bear a grudge. 'She could hardly have been expected to realise you had Jonathan tucked away inside your jacket.' She turned to Jenny with a conspiratorial smile.

'And that's only because he flatly refuses to wheel a pram—he's on his way to do some shopping.'

'Someone has to do it,' growled Jamie. 'There's precious little of anything in the flat.'

'I keep telling you, I'd have happily done it if you'd left me a list!' exclaimed Mandy, her glance somewhat uncertain as it leapt from one to the other.

'You're not employed as a housekeeper,' snapped Jamie. 'Jenny should have thought about it.'

Mandy's eyes met Jenny's, both pairs mirroring their disbelief. She gave an uncomfortable shrug. 'I'm sorry, but I'm afraid I'm meeting someone—I'll have to dash. See you in the morning.'

She leaned across and patted the downy head snuggled into the jacket and, as she walked past the still speechless Jenny, murmured from the side of her mouth. 'I'd suggest counting up to at least a thousand before saying anything.'

'Well, don't just stand there gazing into space,' hectored Jamie as Mandy disappeared. 'We've shopping to do and the supermarket will be closing soon.'

'How dare you—?'

'And for God's sake don't start chanting "how dare you?" at me!' he exclaimed impatiently, striding off. 'I'd have thought you'd already made a big enough fool of yourself—'

'How dare you assume it's my duty to do the shopping?' exploded Jenny, racing after him. '*I* work all day, as does Mandy—though God knows how with you under her feet all day! Why the hell couldn't you have stirred yourself earlier and done it?'

Even as he turned and gave her a shrivelling look, she was already recoiling from the stridency rendering her own tones barely recognisable.

'You really are a glutton for punishment,' he informed

her icily as she caught up with him. 'Just because I should be in Rio now doesn't alter the fact that I have a business to run in Newhaven. I haven't, as you appear to think, been lounging around the place ogling Mandy—I've been commuting between here and the boat-yard for the past several days.'

Stung by his withering tone, Jenny leapt straight into the attack, even though in her heart of hearts she knew an apology was called for.

'It seems rather pointless to me—having a flat in London when your business is on the coast—'

'I dare say it might seem pointless to you, but I don't happen to mind the journey,' he cut in harshly. 'And anyway, I was simply pointing out—hell, what's the point?' he exploded suddenly. 'If you can't open your mouth without making remarks that are either fatuous or erroneous, I suggest you keep it shut!'

They arrived at the supermarket in frigid silence.

'I'll take Jonathan—you can take the trolley,' snapped Jenny as they entered.

'No—you take the wretched thing,' retorted Jamie. 'He'll only bawl the place down if we start disturbing him.'

'One wonders how you'd have managed if I hadn't turned up,' Jenny ground out from between clenched teeth as she resignedly took the trolley.

'Does one?' drawled Jamie, gazing around him with the fascination of one patently unused to such places.

'Where's your shopping list?' demanded Jenny.

'In my head,' he replied, hitching the baby more comfortably against him.

'Well, I'm afraid you'll have to lead me to where everything is,' stated Jenny, suddenly beginning almost to enjoy herself as he flashed her a look of alarm. This was probably not only his first visit here, but to any such place, she gloated, deciding that his housekeeper, on holiday until he was due back from Rio, no doubt did the bulk of his shopping for him. 'I've never been here before,' she added with innocent helplessness.

'Well, I haven't the faintest idea where things are,' he snapped. 'But fortunately everything appears to be signposted.' He gazed around. 'We need a load more nappies,' he muttered, then marched off without so much as a glance in her direction.

After they had located the nappies he announced they needed fruit. From the fruit and vegetable section they trundled all the way back to the baby products for baby oil—then retraced their steps for vegetables.

'For heaven's sake, Jamie!' she exploded as he remembered yet another baby product they needed. 'Would you mind telling me exactly *all* that we need so that we can at least do this intelligently?'

The instant she had finished making her perfectly reasonable demand, Jonathan let out one of his deafening roars, so precisely on cue that the uncharitable thought occurred to her that his patently bored uncle might well have had a hand in causing it.

'Hell, this is all I need,' groaned Jamie.

'All *you* need?' Jenny almost shrieked, and was immediately and mortifyingly conscious of the curious stares of nearby shoppers. 'Jamie, just tell me what we need and get Jonathan out of here before he deafens everyone,' she pleaded.

Half smirking and seemingly oblivious of his nephew's ear-splitting roars, he rattled off a list and then strolled out of the shop.

By the time Jenny had finished, she was feeling decidedly frayed—Jamie and Jonathan, on the other hand, were a picture of contentment, seated on a bench outside and surrounded by adoring females.

'Here comes Mummy with all your goodies,' cooed one of them as Jenny, feeling an affinity with a pack-horse, staggered laden towards them.

'And isn't Mummy lucky to have Daddy here to look after you while she does the shopping?' cooed another—a remark that left Jenny speechless with disbelief.

'Hello, lucky Mummy,' murmured Jamie, grinning up at her evilly. 'I forgot to ask you to get some Camembert.'

'And no doubt you'd be quite happy for me to traipse back in there and get you some,' snapped Jenny, depositing the several carrier bags at her feet.

'I suppose we'd have been better off bringing the car,' he mused, ignoring her gibe as he glanced down at the bags. 'Are you sure you can manage them?'

'Jamie!' she growled warningly.

'Only joking,' he chuckled, rising to his feet and handing her the baby. 'Though I must remember to let you have my car keys when I leave,' he added, picking up the bags.

'When exactly are you due to go back to Brazil?' asked Jenny as they entered the flat.

'Day after tomorrow—why?'

'Why?' she echoed warily, shifting the baby against her as she watched Jamie deposit the bags on the kitchen table. 'Jamie, I've a feeling that pretty soon I might be working well into the evenings.'

'What on—an advertising campaign, or lover-boy?'

'And therefore,' continued Jenny, resolutely ignoring that deliberately provocative question, 'I should like to know how long you'll be away.'

'Come to think of it,' he exclaimed, glancing across at her with a studiously innocent grin, 'it's hardly likely to be lover-boy.'

'And why not?' demanded Jenny, before she could stop herself.

'Well, you're hardly breaking any records for togetherness—one date in—'

'For your information, I happen to see him every day!' she hurled at him, hating him for his smug self-confidence. 'Damn it, Jamie, all I'm asking is how many days you'll be away!'

'It depends on the weather,' he replied, his eyes narrowing coldly as they inspected her. 'Don't you think you should start getting Jonathan ready for bed? I'll get cracking on his bottle.'

It was only the presence of the baby in her arms that stopped Jenny from losing her temper completely.

'I thought we were supposed to be co-operating over looking after him,' she stated, her voice trembling from the force of the control she was exercising over herself. 'Surely you can give me *some* idea as to how long you'll be gone.'

'Let's see, now,' he pondered theatrically. 'The fastest this particular race has ever been completed is two days—the slowest five...but that was the year Hurricane Charlie veered a bit further south than expected.'

'Are you saying you could be away for the best part of a week?' she demanded icily, wondering if he had any idea how lucky he was she was holding Jonathan in her arms.

'I'd say that was most unlikely,' he drawled, 'unless there's another hurricane in the offing no one's aware of.'

Realising she was wasting her time trying to get a straight answer out of him, she turned on her heel.

'Jenny!'

With a barely stifled exclamation of impatience, she halted by the door.

'Why don't you come right out with it and admit you consider it an odds-on certainty that I'll let you down?'

'I would, if I thought it would do me any good.'

'Well, if the worst comes to the worst—as you seem sure it will—perhaps your boyfriend can bail you out at work...or is he merely one of the office boys?'

'He happens to own the company, if you must know,' she hissed, shaking with rage. 'But, unlike you, I don't go in for manipulating other people!' she flung over her shoulder as she marched out of the room.

She bathed and dressed the baby for bed, a task she had come to love as she gained more confidence in handling him. But it was a pleasure that was greatly diminished that evening by the restless churning of her thoughts.

She sat down on one of the beds, despondently conscious of a residual shaking still in her hands as she cuddled her nephew to her.

It just wasn't fair, she protested to herself in a burst of untypical helplessness. For almost as long as she could remember, she had been saddled with feelings of one sort or another for Jamie...and she might as well face the fact that he had blighted her entire adult life! It was pointless trying to fool herself any longer that there was something inherently wonderful about his personality that had caused her to judge all other men against him because, as he had rightly pointed out, she couldn't really claim to know him really closely...the plain truth was that the other men hadn't lacked anything; they simply weren't Jamie.

To be obsessed with him during adolescence was understandable...even at nineteen she could have been excused. But at twenty-three to be in a state where she couldn't make up her mind whether it was love, infatuation or, at times, downright hatred she felt for a man whose lifestyle, despite all his success, was reckless to an extreme and who changed his women as some men changed their shirts...that was cause for definite alarm!

And to crown it all, her brain seemed to stop functioning whenever he was around...all those lies about her experiences with other men...and Gil Wardale of all people!

'I know exactly how you feel,' she sighed as the baby whimpered softly in her arms. 'But it's a good job I don't seek the solution to my problems where you do— in a bottle.'

CHAPTER FIVE

'THAT sauce was delicious—you're very good at them,' said Jenny in rather stilted tones as they finished their meal—one conducted in virtual silence.

On the rare occasions Jamie had undertaken to provide a meal, what he had produced had been of a consistently high standard and invariably Italian.

'Perhaps we should indulge in a recipe-swapping session one of these days,' he replied, in a decidedly challenging tone. 'That thing you concocted the other day was—how shall I put it?—interesting.'

Jenny's expression tightened angrily in the face of such total rejection of the olive branch she had proffered. The 'thing' to which he had so provokingly referred had been her one and only flop—a sweet and sour dish from which she had inadvertently omitted the sour ingredients.

'I'll write you out the recipe just as soon as I've cleared these,' she flung at him from between clenched teeth, rising and starting to clear the table. 'Would you like fruit or something?'

He shook his head, rising also.

'There's not that much to cooking, really, other than being able to read a recipe,' he muttered to himself as he helped clear the table.

'So how is it that some people—who are perfectly able to read—simply can't cook?' demanded Jenny.

'They'd soon find out they could if the need ever really arose,' he replied dismissively. 'What those who claim they can't cook are actually saying is that cooking doesn't appeal to them.'

Jenny stacked the dishwasher, puzzled by a relentless air of challenge in him...if he wanted to pick a fight, surely he could have chosen a subject a little more contentious than cooking!

'But it obviously appeals to you,' she stated, despite a feeling of complete certainty that he would automatically disagree—which he did instantly.

'It holds no appeal whatever for me. It's merely something I do if and when I have to.'

'If that's the case, I'm surprised you're so good at Italian food,' retorted Jenny, her tone every bit as sharp as his had been. 'I'd have thought someone with your views would have gone in for something a lot more basic.'

'It is basic to me—because the only book I could lay my hands on when I first had to cook was one on Italian cookery. Do you want this coffee in here or in the living-room?'

'In the living-room,' she replied, and began preparing a tray. 'You should have consulted your sister—she has a fantastic collection of cookery books.'

'Hell!' he exclaimed, startling her. 'I forgot to mention that Clare rang just as I got back this evening. She's managed to organise a flying visit for the day after tomorrow.'

Jenny's face softened perceptibly. 'Poor Clare, she must be missing Jonathan like mad,' she sighed. 'What time is she due?'

'She wasn't able to say,' replied Jamie, placing the coffee-pot on the tray. 'She's hitching a lift on one of the supply planes—and going back with it the same day—so I suppose she'll simply have to fit in with their schedule.' He picked up the tray. 'Unfortunately, I shan't be around to see her—I'm catching an early flight out to Rio.'

Jenny followed him into the sitting-room, her expression troubled.

'And there's absolutely no chance of my having any time off work,' she fretted.

'That's what you get for working for slave-drivers,' observed Jamie caustically as he set down the tray. 'Not that it matters—because, apart from checking on her son and heir, Clare wants to spend some time with Mandy. She's thinking along the lines of asking her to join them on a permanent basis in Belgium.'

'I'm sure she'll take to Mandy immediately,' said Jenny, deciding to let his remark about her job pass as she began pouring the coffee.

'The way you did?' murmured Jamie.

Jenny slammed down the coffee-pot. 'That's it! I've had enough of you and your snide remarks. You seem to think...' It was as her words came to a peculiarly choked halt that she made the humiliating discovery that she was actually in tears.

'You can switch off the waterworks,' Jamie informed her coldly, striding to her side and grasping her by the arms. 'They might work on some men, but I simply find them irritating.'

Beside herself with fury, Jenny tore free an arm and had hit him full across the face before she had time to realise what she was doing.

'Just thank your lucky stars I didn't hit you back,' he snarled, wrestling her wildly struggling form to a painfully enforced stillness against him. 'Because, I can assure you, my every instinct told me to do precisely that!'

'If it'll make you feel any better, go ahead and do so,' choked Jenny rashly.

'Do you honestly think trading blows is going to make

either of us feel any better?' he demanded, the unmistakable hint of laughter in his words startling her.

'Jamie, I'm sorry…I really didn't mean to do that,' she blurted out, full awareness of what she had done only now sinking in. 'I've never even raised my hand in anger before, let alone hit anyone. If only you wouldn't keep niggling on at me all the time…I just—'

'Hey!' he protested, drawing her a little away from him to gaze down at her from eyes that managed to twinkle even while maintaining their guarded watchfulness. 'Is this meant to be an apology—or what?'

'I'm apologising,' she whispered abjectly, appalled by the thought of what she had done and even more so by the sight of the reddening patch on his cheek. 'Oh, Jamie, I'm so sorry!' she gasped, raising tentative fingers to explore the damage.

'Careful of that protruding cheekbone,' he warned, though the twinkle had now disappeared completely from his eyes.

Thrown by his look, Jenny found herself unable even to attempt a suitably joking response. In fact, she was unable to make any response, she noted with the same almost abstract wariness with which she now noticed her heart was racing like a tom-tom—and certainly not from anger.

'Peace reigns at last,' he murmured, the merest hint of a taunt in the words. 'But for how long? I wonder. You know, Jenny, I never dreamt you had it in you to fight this dirty.'

'I've told you I'm sorry I hit you!' she protested, then let out a gasp of shock as he suddenly pulled her fully against him.

'But I warn you, no one can fight dirtier than I can when I set my mind to it,' he murmured, with an ease totally divorced from the urgent message of arousal his body was so blatantly imparting to hers.

Jenny opened her mouth to protest that she had no idea what he was talking about; all that came out was a choked cry as her body awoke to his with a force that shuddered through her.

'You see, you're the one who's supposed to be seducing me, not I you—remember?' he continued with that same disconcertingly detached ease.

'I'm not supposed to be doing any such thing!' she protested agitatedly, her mind and her body pulling in diametrically opposed directions.

'Jenny, you claim your attitudes to relationships are no different from mine,' he pointed out, the reasonableness of his tone so at odds with the seductive ardency of his body that her mind seized up in total confusion. 'Could it be that it's wishful thinking on my part that leads me to misread your response to me?'

His hands played against her back as he spoke, the lightness of their caressing touch adding yet another confusing dimension to the chaos bombarding her every sense.

'Perhaps it's simple revulsion that causes you to quiver in my arms?' he murmured, while his hands and body continued their relentless assault on her senses. 'Perhaps it's—'

'Jamie, why don't you just shut up?' she exclaimed defeatedly, clasping his head in her hands and dragging it down to hers.

'Just as long as you promise to be gentle with me,' he chuckled—a chuckle that deteriorated into a soft groan the instant their lips met.

It didn't really matter, she thought wildly as he took swift command, the bruising urgency of his mouth never once abating as he manoeuvred their locked bodies down on to the sofa. Nothing mattered at all—not this alien desperation galvanising her body as it sought for the answers to unknown questions in the burning sanctuary of his—nothing, save this man and the magic he had always held for her.

It both shocked and excited her, the single-minded purposefulness with which his impatient hands stripped her eagerly co-operative body down to no more than her briefs. And it shocked and excited her even more, the undisguised urgency with which her own hands aided his to perform the same task on him.

But it was the effect on her of skin against naked skin, and the force of the insatiable need pounding through her, that brought gasped cries of protest spilling from her as sanity finally deserted her totally.

'Jenny,' he whispered hoarsely, his hands raking the length of her body, his teeth biting with punishing passion on her flesh while a litany of incoherent words poured from him. 'Damn it, Jenny!' he exclaimed suddenly, raising his head and glowering down at her. 'I'm not giving in!'

'Don't be so infantile,' she whispered, breathless yet supremely confident as she wound her arms around his neck and tried to draw his head down to hers.

'No!' he growled, shaking his head fiercely, even as he began lowering it, now of his own accord. 'I want to resist you…but I'm not sure I can,' he protested.

'You can't,' she whispered, though her words came out more pleading than confident.

'I know I can't, but—'

The sudden ring of the telephone interrupted his words, freezing both their bodies; then he began laughing softly.

'Jamie, no!' she protested as he made to leave her. 'Please…don't answer it!'

For an instant she thought he would heed her as his body seemed to relax against hers; then he tore himself free.

'Who says there's no such thing as a guardian angel?' he demanded on a breathless attempt at a laugh.

He picked up the entire instrument, striding with it to the far end of the large room before barking out his name into it.

'Polly, my angel—where have you been hiding?'

Jenny hauled herself upright. Polly, his angel, she thought with a flash of murderous rage, only to have a wry voice point out from within her that, after his reference to a guardian angel, the words were obviously intended for her ears. The rage dying in her as swiftly as it had arisen, she huddled into a corner of the sofa, her lungs replenishing themselves with painful gasps, while tidal waves of numbness and incomprehension washed over both her mind and body.

'Yes, of course we must get together, my sweet,' Jamie was crooning into the mouthpiece.

And he was doing it deliberately, knowing that she couldn't help but hear, she told herself with a sickening lack of conviction. Had the phone not rung, there was no way he would ever have found the strength to resist her, she consoled herself. She relaxed a fraction, allowing herself to savour that fact, then suddenly stiffened in horror, a strangled groan of disbelief slipping from her. What on earth was she thinking? Had her senses deserted her completely?

Her wide-spaced blue eyes huge with shock, she gazed down at herself...here she was, virtually naked, and actually seeking to console herself with the fact that only the interruption of the telephone had saved not herself, but Jamie, from their making love!

Her dazed eyes moved across the room, lingering on

the tall, magnificently proportioned body clad only in
snowy white boxer shorts. And then something within
her capitulated and she made no attempt to divert them
as they clung and feasted.

'OK, I'll ring you when I get back from Rio.' He
replaced the receiver and dropped the telephone down
on to a nearby chair, then turned to face her. 'And while
I'm on the subject of my return from Rio, I want lover-
boy out of your life by then…I've no intention of subjecting myself to this ridiculous carry-on again,' he informed her, his face now entirely devoid of any trace of
the passion that had so recently softened it.

Jenny let out a squeak of impotent rage.

'And who am I supposed to console myself with when
you're off gallivanting with lover-girl and sundry others?' she flung at him, once she had regained control
over her vocal cords.

'Polly's simply a friend,' he informed her icily.

'Oh, yes?' exploded Jenny. 'Silly me! I'd forgotten—
you always call friends "my sweet" and "my angel"!'

She watched as he began strolling towards her, an
acute sense of being under threat forming itself from
within the mishmash of negative emotions assailing her.

'I've no idea why, but the last thing I expected was
that you'd turn out to have such a jealous nature,' he
stated almost conversationally.

Jenny glared up at him as he came to a halt before
her, then reached out and grabbed the nearest thing to
her—his shirt—clutching it to her. To her utter mortifi-
cation, he began laughing.

'Jenny, I…' He broke off, shaking his head before
raking his fingers through his hair in a gesture of per-
plexity.

'You what?' she demanded acidly, inwardly berating

herself for not having had the sense to dash from the room while he had been on the telephone.

'Anyone unaware of the true facts would take one look at you curled up there and probably get a picture of a maiden determinedly protecting her honour.'

Which, paradoxically, was precisely how she was beginning to feel, thought Jenny confusedly. Feeling obliged to repudiate at least one of the two statements he had made, she opted for the first as marginally safer.

'There's nothing in the least jealous about my nature,' she informed him with all the hauteur she could muster.

'Oh, no? Since the moment you clapped eyes on Mandy, you've never stopped—'

'I've already admitted I was wrong about her,' she leapt in defensively, now castigating herself for not having had the sense to keep her mouth shut, instead of letting herself in for this. 'I was being over-protective of Jonathan.'

'Bull,' he retorted, chuckling. 'And what about Polly?'

'I was merely objecting to your double standards!' she almost shrieked at him. 'Why should there be one rule for me and—?'

'Does whatsis name—Bill?—get subjected to this manic possessiveness of yours?' he enquired mildly, almost as though he was unaware she had been speaking.

'His name's *Gil*—as in Gilbert! And stop twisting everything I say!'

He shrugged, a look both speculative and slightly wary on his face as he began walking away.

'Whatever his name is—just make sure you're rid of him by the time I return.' He paused as he reached the door, his back to her as he continued. 'And another thing—I can think of few greater turn-offs in a woman than possessiveness.'

It was the cold-blooded arrogance of those words that embedded itself in her and from which she found it impossible to shake free her thoughts. It was the complete and utter gall of it! He had ordered her to remove from her life the man for whom she had implied, if not love, at least strong feelings—which of the two, she could no longer recall—yet obviously saw no contradiction in warning her against being possessive!

It was several hours into the restless wakefulness of the night before her indignation had abated sufficiently to allow the events that had preceded that arrogant statement to filter back into her mind…and it was then that she began experiencing feelings of fear and utter hopelessness.

Up until this very moment, she would have sworn it was her nature to face head-on whatever life threw in her path…but could she honestly claim that where Jamie was concerned? She had tried, at nineteen, with what she now saw as cringe-making recklessness, to deal openly with her feelings for him…yet had done a complete about-turn and retreated into a shell at his rejection of her. She would have claimed to be neither jealous nor possessive…yet her gut reaction to the sight of him with Mandy, to hearing him speak to Polly, hardly supported such a claim. And what constituted her true nature anyway? There was a part of her, hitherto unsuspected, that now wanted him—physically needed him—with an intensity that was unfettered either by the merest hint of shame or the slightest thought of prudence…she, whose sexual experience was completely nil! That the root of her virtual inexperience at any romantic level with men was tied up in the confused jumble of her feelings for Jamie was something she now had to accept without question. But it was her inability to do anything but accept unquestioningly what she became in his arms—

would always become in his arms—that was beginning to terrify the wits out of her.

But there was one, long forgotten element in her nature that began stirring defensively within her—a tendency she had often resorted to as a child: to clown her way out of trouble when the going got really tough. Oddly enough, it was the memory of the miserable success rate of those tactics that made her welcome their sudden stirring within her—they had more often than not only exacerbated the trouble she was in by infuriating beyond measure her parents, teachers or whoever was on the receiving end of them.

Jamie arrived home unusually late the following evening. Jonathan was bathed, fed and sound asleep, and in the little-used dining-room the darkly gleaming rosewood table was set for two. In the oven simmered a carefully prepared casserole of chicken.

'My God, how could you be so cruel? How could you do this to me?' were the words with which she accosted him in the hallway, where he was removing his coat.

His entire body froze, his arms not fully from his coat sleeves, and his mouth looked on the verge of gaping open in shock.

'I know it's another woman! What's her name? You might as well tell me it, because I'll only hire a private detective if you don't!'

'I wonder what the rates are for following the suspect to Rio,' he murmured, completing the removal of his coat now that he had regained his equilibrium. 'It's funny,' he added with an almost affectionate chuckle. 'I'd almost forgotten that kooky side to you.'

'Stop trying to distract me!' she exclaimed with theatrical indignation. 'I've been slaving over a hot stove all evening while you've been out womanising!'

'Can it, Jenny,' he groaned, though there was notice-able laughter in his plea. 'I've had a pig of a day and I'm just not in the mood.'

'*You've* had a pig of a day?' she continued in the same vein, though finding keeping up the momentum of the mood she had spent several hours whipping herself into now perilously difficult.

'OK, have it your way,' he grinned, striding towards her and then prostrating himself at her feet. 'I give in—her name was Desdemona Crumpet and she led me astray. But I swear I'll never so much as see her again, if only you'll feed me.' He heaved himself to his feet. 'I hope you meant that bit about slaving over a hot stove—I'm starving!' he grinned.

'Desdemona Crumpet,' murmured Jenny, now even more distracted from her self-imposed role by the fact that her heart was racing fit to break all records. 'Desdemona Crum—'

'Jenny!' he groaned pleadingly, slipping an arm round her shoulders.

'Oh, all right, then—I'll forgive you,' she babbled breathlessly, acutely conscious that her plans were back-firing on her...and disastrously.

'Thank heavens for that,' he breathed, turning her slowly towards him. 'You really are an evil little tyke—but then I doubt if you need me to tell you that,' he whispered as his mouth sought hers.

'I thought you were supposed to be starving,' she quipped, having to conjure up will-power she was un-aware of possessing in order to evade those seeking lips.

'And I thought you were supposed to be hell-bent on seducing me,' he protested huskily.

'Before supper?' she exclaimed, aghast, pushing him away from her while she still had the strength.

'You should try me now,' he coaxed, laughing, 'while my resistance is at its lowest.'

'My, my, Desdemona really must have given you a hard time of it,' she breezed, darting off towards the kitchen.

Once in there, she took several gulping breaths in an attempt to steady herself. The whole idea of this ridiculous performance to which she had just subjected herself was to infuriate him—to punish him for the chaos he was wreaking on her—not to have him join in, she reflected agitatedly.

And now where was she? Seconds ago, it had taken every shred of will-power she possessed simply to escape his light-hearted—and rather half-hearted, come to think of it—attempt to steal a kiss!

'Where's that food, or are you deliberately trying to drive me back into Miss Crumpet's arms by withholding it?' he demanded from the doorway scarcely five minutes later.

He had changed into faded denims and a navy sweatshirt and his hair was tousled and damply curling from showering.

With considerable effort, Jenny composed her face to sternness.

'Sorry, but I simply refuse to feed you until you're suitably dressed for dinner,' she announced, wondering how long she was capable of continuing with this charade and realising she was going to have to, now that she had started it, even if it killed her.

Less than another five minutes later, he joined her in the dining-room—this time dressed in a dinner jacket and looking so devastatingly attractive that Jenny felt the breath freeze in her lungs.

'*Now* will you feed me?' he demanded pleadingly.

Jenny opened her mouth to make a flippant remark and nothing happened.

'Jenny, please...I'm starved!' he groaned, clutching his stomach theatrically.

Her mind racing to find something with which to tide herself over until she recovered her wits, she pursed her lips and blew.

'Jennifer! This is—'

'Shut up, will you?' she muttered, relieved to find she still had powers of speech, pursing her lips and blowing once more. 'I'm trying to give you a wolf-whistle.'

'Feed me, then afterwards I'll teach you how.'

It was only when she finally retired to bed that the terrible tension under which she had been snapped and she buried her face in her pillow and sobbed as she hadn't since she was a small child.

All that ridiculous performance...and for what? Ever since Vienna she had been a bag of nerves: one minute dithering and confused, the next strident and aggressive; and in between she had managed to concoct a tissue of lies around herself that turned her into something she wasn't and which compromised her integrity. At sixteen she had had no problems facing up to reality...so why all the problems now that she was twenty-three? Except that loving Jamie Castile when she was sixteen had seemed as natural as breathing: at twenty-three it seemed an open invitation to heartbreak.

'Jenny!' Clare Page reached into the hall to greet her sister-in-law, Jonathan in her arms.

'Clare, I'm so sorry I couldn't manage to get away any earlier,' apologised Jenny, hugging them both.

'Don't worry—I understand,' murmured Clare, frowning suddenly as she stepped back to look at Jenny. 'You look exhausted, love!' she exclaimed guiltily. 'Has this little monster of mine been depriving you of sleep?'

'I promise you, Clare, his monster nights are a thing of the past—he sleeps right through,' said Jenny, smiling a bright, forced smile. She knew exactly how ghastly she had looked this morning and, suspecting the conclusions Clare would draw from it, had prayed she would recover as the day wore on.

Her heart sank as Clare flashed her a guilt-laden look, then glanced down at her sleeping son.

'Actually, I was just about to put him to bed,' she said. 'I'm afraid he missed a few of his naps today, thanks to my presence.'

'You do that and I'll make us some tea,' smiled Jenny, removing her coat.

She felt cold and tired and wet and miserable, she thought dejectedly, and those were her more positive feelings. But she was going to have to pull herself together if she was to reassure Clare, she decided firmly, and began making the tea.

'How did you get on with Mandy?' she asked, when Clare later joined her in the sitting-room.

'Marvellously,' replied Clare, sitting down beside her on the sofa and pouring the tea. 'She's coming to work for us in Brussels—she's thrilled with the idea of working abroad...milk?'

Jenny nodded. 'What time is your plane back this evening—have we time for a meal?'

Clare shook her head and glanced at her watch. 'Mandy and I ate at lunchtime and Clive—the co-pilot who dropped me off—is picking me up again in just over an hour.' She smiled apologetically. 'The whole day's been a bit of a mad rush—but it's been worth every second with Jonathan.'

'Oh, Clare—it must be terrible for you being parted from him like this,' sympathised Jenny.

'It is. But I'm hoping it won't be for too much longer,' replied Clare, glancing at her anxiously. 'Jenny, perhaps Mandy would agree to moving to Brussels before Graham and I leave—'

'Clare!' groaned Jenny indignantly—then pulled a small face. 'I know the way your mind works and I know you're equating the ghastly way I look with Jonathan—and most unfairly, because he's been a perfect angel day and night. He most certainly isn't the reason I didn't sleep a wink last night…I wouldn't lie to you over something like that!'

'So—why *didn't* you get a wink of sleep last night?' asked Clare casually, picking up her cup and taking a sip from it, her eyes never once leaving Jenny.

'Oh—this and that—I shan't bore you with the details,' muttered Jenny dismissively. 'Now tell me—how are things progressing in Czechoslovakia?'

'Far better than any of us dared hope,' replied Clare. 'But it's not something I feel up to chatting about on my one day off…I hope you don't mind.'

'Oh, Clare—I'm sorry!' exclaimed Jenny guiltily. 'Of course I don't—I should have realised!'

Clare gave an understanding smile, then replaced her cup in its saucer. 'Jenny, are you and Jamie having problems?' she asked quietly.

'Clare, I *promise* you, Jonathan's been an absolute angel—we both adore him!'

'I know you do, but I didn't ask if you and Jamie were having problems with Jonathan,' pointed out Clare gently.

'I suppose Jamie and I bicker a bit, but it's nothing I can't handle,' conceded Jenny reluctantly. 'I'm probably a far cry from the sophisticated women he's used to,' she added with a nervous laugh—and immediately wished she hadn't.

'I hope he's not leaving you to do all the chores,' said Clare, her eyes, an exact replica of those of her brother, watchful.

'No—he cooks fairly regularly, though he needs a bit of prodding to do other things.'

Clare's eyes widened perceptibly. 'He cooks, does he? Italian food?'

Jenny nodded. 'He says it was the only cookbook he could find.'

'The only cookbook he could find when he was twelve,' murmured Clare, a hollow, oddly sad note in her words. 'And, if I know my brother, the first and last one he's ever likely to consult.'

'I'm afraid I don't understand,' muttered Jenny, feeling faintly ill-at-ease—something she had never before felt in the company of her gentle, always approachable sister-in-law.

'I tend to forget how much younger you are,' sighed Clare, reaching over and patting her reassuringly on the hand. 'I was only eight, and Jamie twelve, when our father died.'

And Jamie was twelve when he'd learned—had had to learn—to cook, reflected Jenny, a feeling that was soft and sad and unlike any other she had ever experienced drifting through her.

'Even when Dad was alive, we used to fluctuate between being princes and virtual paupers—though, from the warmth and love with which we were surrounded, Jamie and I only regarded our fluctuating circumstances as rather exciting,' continued Clare. 'But just about every penny he possessed was tied up in one of Dad's schemes when he died and we were left with practically nothing.'

As she listened to Clare's words, Jenny found herself trying to picture Jamie—the man she loved—at twelve.

'Even during the really lean times, we'd always had a housekeeper—well, someone to do the cooking—simply because Mother swore she was incapable of doing it herself.'

Jenny gave an involuntary smile; it was something she could well imagine the vague, ethereally beautiful Constance Castile claiming and getting away with.

'The housekeeper was the first economy Jamie decided on—mainly, I think, because he loathed the woman. But, of course, it was he who ultimately had to take on the chore.'

'Aided by his Italian cookbook,' murmured Jenny, hastily lowering her head as she furiously blinked back tears.

'Yes. He even eventually managed to persuade Mother that, if a twelve-year-old boy could master it, there was no reason why she couldn't,' chuckled Clare. 'You know, I honestly used to think he'd never so much as boil an egg again, once he'd got Mother to take over…you can imagine how little a task as sissy as cooking would appeal to your average macho twelve-year-old—and believe me, Jamie was the most macho of them all!'

'But what did you live on?' asked Jenny, horrified.

'After about a couple of years, Dad's last scheme started paying dividends—a pittance at first, but now Mother's very comfortably off, thanks to it…not that it could ever bring back the part of her that died along with Dad.'

'She must have loved him so much,' mused Jenny wistfully.

'Oh, she loved him all right—and still does,' sighed Clare, the edge to her voice startling Jenny. 'She went completely to pieces after he died…which goes a long way to accounting for Jamie's subsequent behaviour. Not that there wasn't the element of recklessness in him long before Dad died, and which neither of them showed much inclination to curb; but so much responsibility was heaped on him after Dad's death—far too much for one so young—and it was a pretty sure bet that someone of Jamie's temperament would end up periodically running wild, simply as a safety valve.'

'But he's done fantastically well for himself as an adult,' said Jenny, racked by terrible guilt as she recalled her taunting accusations of irresponsibility.

'Yes, he has—materially,' agreed Clare with a sigh. 'But that's not the area that worries me. He's never been able to sustain a relationship with a woman—and the blame for that is entirely his. Jenny, I honestly think love is something that terrifies him. He seems only to have been left with the negative aspects of our parents' love…he seems to have forgotten all the incredible joy they shared so openly and to remember only the devastation that the losing of so much brought to our mother.' Her face tense and unhappy, Clare picked up her cup once more and drained it.

Not trusting herself to comment, Jenny did the same.

'I honestly don't know what's got into me,' exclaimed Clare with an embarrassed little laugh that was most unlike her. She began pouring them both another cup of tea. 'Perhaps it's because sitting around and talking is a luxury we simply haven't the time for in the medical camp that I'm rambling on like this.' She gave a sad shake of her head. 'Or perhaps it's just that Graham and I have such a wonderful relationship and I can't help wanting the same for Jamie…and for you too, love… you mean so much to me,' she added softly. 'Is there anybody special in your life?'

Jenny dropped her eyes, then shook her head.

'I suppose, in my heart of hearts, I was hoping you'd say there was,' sighed Clare. 'Part of me has always prayed that you'd get over my beautiful mixed-up brother…while another part of me…' She broke off, reaching out and putting her arm round Jenny. 'I'm sure you know what that other part of me was praying for…and at least now you know something about what makes him the way he is…and who knows? Perhaps there's still hope.'

CHAPTER SIX

JENNY heard on the early-morning news that Jamie and his crew had won the race. She wondered if he would ring her, but he didn't.

'I'm going to miss you, Cuddles Page, even if you can be a little monkey at times—such as now,' she told her nephew as she tucked him into his cot for the third time that night. 'And to think I told your Mummy you were a little angel!' she chuckled, as he gurgled contentedly up at her, showing no inclination towards sleep. 'It's nearly eleven o'clock and I want some sleep even if you don't.'

The instant she reached the door and switched off the light, he roared like a tyrant.

It really wasn't like him, she fretted, torn as to what to do. Perhaps he was teething, she thought anxiously; he had been a bit clingy all evening...though Mandy would have mentioned something like that. Perhaps it was her fault! She had hardly been a bundle of joy for the past few days. Filled with guilt at the thought that she might have transferred her own tension to him, she went back to the cot and lifted him out, cuddling his rage-rigid little body to her.

'There, there, it's all right—Auntie Jenny will stay with you until you feel all safe and secure.'

At least tomorrow was Saturday and she wouldn't have to go to work, she thought with relief as she lay down on one of the beds with the baby in her arms.

'My, that's a miraculous recovery you're making,' she

whispered. 'Perhaps you'd like to tell me what all that was about.'

She chuckled as he emitted an almost contented-sounding hiccup.

'OK, if that's the way you feel about it—perhaps I should tell you my troubles instead.'

She reached over and grabbed the quilt from the cot and tucked it around the baby and wondered how she was likely to fare if this became a prolonged session. The air had recently taken on that sharp, almost acrid scent of October and had turned from mellowness to blustery cold—and she was wearing a summer-weight housecoat.

'I might need you as a hot-water bottle for my feet,' she informed her silent, though somewhat active, companion. 'I suppose it's lovely and hot where your uncle is...which brings us right back to my problems.'

Clare's words had affected her deeply and in many ways, though none more strangely than their coming almost as a confirmation of something she had already known.

'Though why I'm getting in such a state over his having a hang-up about loving is beyond me. The truth is, Cuddles, that even if he didn't I wouldn't have stood much of a chance, given the calibre of the opposition queueing up to get their hands on him.'

She laughed as a tiny foot dug her hard in the ribs.

'You needn't think I'm fishing for compliments,' she protested. 'I know I'm not bad-looking—on a good day I've even been described as a knock-out...but some of those women with their sights on your uncle...now they're what you call gorgeous. And a lot of them have hair like Mandy's—long and glamorous—whereas I've never had the patience to grow mine again ever since I had my plaits cut off when I was fourteen. And...' She broke off with an exclamation of disbelief. Why was she babbling away like this to a baby? And why was she claiming she would have stood no chance with Jamie? He was just as powerfully attracted to her as she was to him...even if love didn't happen to feature in what he felt.

She woke up with a start, disturbed to sense the warmth of the baby's body leaving hers.

'Don't be afraid, Uncle Jamie's here,' chuckled Jamie's deep, familiar voice.

'Is he asleep?' asked Jenny groggily, having extreme difficulty finding her bearings.

'Yes—I'm just tucking him into—'

'Jamie, what are you doing here?' she gasped, sitting bolt upright.

'I got a lift in a friend's executive jet—and a very hairy descent into Heathrow it was. It's blowing a gale out there.'

'But you...I...' She slumped back down on the bed, her mind still too sluggish to co-operate.

'Come on, it's time we got you tucked up too,' he chuckled, moving from the cot to stand over her.

'How long have you been back?' she asked confusedly, noticing his apparel—surely he hadn't travelled in a bathrobe?

'About half an hour. I fell into a hot bath and afterwards decided to have a peek at my nephew. Jenny, what's all this about—has he been playing up?'

'He was a bit fretful tonight...heavens, what time is it?'

'Around midnight—I haven't my watch on. Come on, it's time you were in bed.'

Ignoring the hand he held out to her, Jenny swung her legs off the bed, then let out a groan.

'What's wrong?' demanded Jamie, reaching down and catching hold of her.

'I seem to have seized up,' she muttered, wishing her heart had too as it began pounding out of control. 'Leave me alone—I'll manage.'

His response was to lift her up in his arms.

'Jenny, you're like a block of ice!' he exclaimed exasperatedly. 'Why the hell didn't you cover yourself up properly?' he demanded, carrying her from the room.

'Because it wasn't my intention to fall asleep like that,' she protested, then flung her arms tightly around his neck as he suddenly stooped to open the door to her room.

'That's right, cling tight,' he murmured huskily, kicking the door shut behind him before carrying her across to the bed. 'That's just the sort of welcome I could do with—one that I'd have flown here under my own steam for.'

'What, just flapped your wings and flown?' she asked dizzily, soaring high on a cloud of mind-blowing happiness. He had missed her!

'Just flapped my wings and flown,' he confirmed, laughing as he fell heavily on to the bed with her still locked in his arms.

The pounding of her heart was causing her severe problems as he uncurled her from his arms and positioned her beside him; its heavy thud was like a stifling pain hammering away inside her. But it was a pain overridden by a breathless, expectant pleasure as she gazed up into his face, its contours darkly shadowed and almost saturnine in the faintness of the light entering the room from the fanlight above the doorway.

'Put your arms around me again—but this time tell me how much you've missed me,' he demanded huskily, his breath fanning hotly against her face.

'What makes you think I've missed you?' she retorted, her words stifled and disjointed and several tones higher than was normal.

'What makes me think that?' he teased, his lips brushing weightlessly against hers before he drew back slightly from her to skim his fingers lightly across the straining tips of her breasts.

He laughed softly at the sharp gasp of pleasure his action brought from her, then unhurriedly untied the belt of her housecoat, freeing her body from the soft cling of its material. Then he lowered his head to her breasts.

'Your body tells me,' he breathed hoarsely, his mouth now caressing impatiently where his fingers had touched.

Whatever her body had told him, it now started shrieking out messages to her, responding with trembling inhibition to the shock waves of pleasure fanning from his mouth and piercing through her flesh with its tormenting sweetness.

'You'll have to help me,' he groaned, his mouth still a moistly exquisite torture against her rigid flesh as he attempted to remove the gown from her entirely.

She responded to his plea as though her life depended on it, shrugging free her arms to clasp them around him.

'Oh, my beautiful, unpredictable Jenny,' he whispered, his words muffled as his mouth pressed moist, exploratory kisses at the base of her throat.

She wondered how he could possibly speak—she had stopped breathing what seemed like a lifetime ago—but it wasn't her seeming inability to breathe that started up the panic suddenly rampaging within her...it was the inconceivable idea that he might suddenly choose to put an end to this crazy, wonderful moment of magic. He had stopped once before, she thought frantically, her hands moving of their own volition to drag the robe from his shoulders.

When he laughed and flung the robe from himself, there was no room in her mind to examine any aspect of her own behaviour; her only awareness was of the panic mounting within her that he might any moment desert her. The fierceness with which she clung to him to prevent such a happening drew laughing protests from him, which in turn only increased her irrational fears.

'No,' she protested, the pent-up air in her lungs exploding from her almost in anger. 'Jamie, don't laugh!'

She didn't want his laughter—not now. There was a fear in her that laughter might be the weapon with which he could blot out his receptiveness to the love demanding total expression within her—a love so powerful that it must surely kindle a reciprocal love in him.

'Jenny, please,' he begged, trying to extricate himself from the fierceness of her hold. 'There's laughter and laughter…and mine…' He broke off with a sharp cry as her body fought to seek the total contact it was being denied with his. 'Jenny, we've waited so long for this moment…I don't want impatience to spoil it.'

'I can't help being impatient,' she gasped, misunderstanding his words as her body got its way and, for the first time in her life, she experienced and responded to with total abandonment the full potency of rampant male desire.

'Darling, it's *my* impatience I'm having the problem with,' he groaned softly, need shuddering tautly through him. 'Yours just makes my task almost impossible.'

It was the capitulation in his words that relaxed her that fraction that allowed the glimmer of a thought to enter the ecstatic confusion of her mind. In giving him her love she would betray herself…her inexperience… her lies.

But it was the sudden sureness with which he now channelled his ardour, his lips and hands coaxing and

urging her onwards, that drove her beyond the point of
any capacity for thought.

'How could I ever think I could resist you?' he demanded feverishly, his hands increasingly purposeful as
they moved against her, preparing her; caressing and tormenting her and bringing soft cries of protest from her
as the need within her was fanned beyond endurance.

Her initial instinct was to resist when he moved to
still her body; then came an intuitive understanding and
his name was a choked cry of shock on her lips as her
body accepted the plundering invasion of his.

And almost in that same instant she heard her name
explode from him as though in angry accusation—a
fleeting moment of consciousness that was lost as her
body recovered in an involuntary, ecstatic welcome of
his.

As though suddenly freed, her untutored body was
responding to his with an almost violent lack of inhibition, peaking and plummeting from one glorious sensation to the next, welcoming each with wild cries of
delight and soft sobs of disbelief.

And it was the intensity of the love within her that
cried out in exultation when she sensed the magic he
was creating from her spread itself to him until it exploded between them in one vast and mutual cascade of
total fulfilment.

She lay locked in his arms, her involuntary need to
sing out with joy rendered impossible by the huge, gulping gasps of air being taken in by her starved lungs.

'Jamie,' she choked out breathlessly, raising her face
from where it had been buried against the silken warmth
of him and gazing up at him. 'Jamie?' she whispered,
that crazy need to sing with joy deserting her.

Even in the dimness of the light she could see the
expressionless mask that was now his face. She could

feel the sharp swell of his chest against her body as his lungs too demanded sustenance…but his face remained immobile, chillingly without any expression.

'You lied to me,' he stated, his words as distant as his masked face as he drew his body from hers, severing those last links of a fast-dying magic.

Completely stunned, she opened her mouth to protest, but was beyond it even registering with her when no sound emerged.

'How could you possibly lie over something like that?' he demanded harshly. 'How many other lies have you been telling me?'

'Dozens!' she hurled at him, pushing out wildly at him as her world began disintegrating around her. 'How dare you?' she cried, pummelling at him with her fists.

'Jenny, I—'

'Get out of here! Get out! What sort of monster are you, for God's sake?'

'Jenny, please…at least talk about it,' he protested, making no attempt to protect himself from her demented blows.

'Get out of here…just leave me. Go!'

She rolled over on to her stomach, burying her face in the pillow, her body sensing the movement of his as he rose from the bed…and then she heard the sound of the door as it closed behind him.

For several minutes she lay there, her body rigid with tension. It was as though she were teetering on the edge of a chasm and if she relaxed she would topple over into a nothingness from which there would be no escape. Four years ago she had felt devastated when he had rejected her. Devastated? She had had no idea of what true devastation entailed until now, she told herself, the anger now welling in her steadying her and drawing her back from the edge.

She suddenly hauled herself upright, the expression on her face mutinous. How dared she let herself get into such a state? She wasn't the first woman to have fallen in love with an insensitive, black-hearted monster—nor the last!

She switched on the light, flinging herself off the bed as she searched for her housecoat. All right, so to him it wasn't such a big deal, her having shared her first moment of physical love with him, she told herself bitterly, angrily belting the gown around her and sitting down on the edge of the bed. But to round on her right after...with such cold, loveless words! Clare was wrong—there could never be any hope for him...no normal human being could have behaved the way he had...he was a complete monster! For several seconds her mind exercised itself by dredging up more and more damningly vituperative words with which to describe him. And then there were no more and she felt her shoulders sag beneath the weight of the terrible hurt now bearing down on her and the humiliating memory of the fear that had gripped her that he might reject her...if only he had! But he had participated without restraint in the love she had lavished on him. And it was the memory of the unbridled passion with which he had participated that began ripping through the shroud of desolation and anger numbing her, and she leapt to her feet, as though by doing so she might escape the treacherous excitement with which her body was now responding to those memories. Tonight—for the first time in her life—she had given total physical expression to the love she had borne him for so long, but in his inability to give love himself it was almost as though he was incapable of recognising the love she had so blatantly offered him...and therein lay the means to her hanging on to at least a shred of her devastated pride.

For several seconds she paced up and down, frowning deeply as she concentrated, then she suddenly squared her shoulders, strode to the door and yanked it open.

She hesitated only for the briefest of instants before marching down the hallway to Jamie's room. Without knocking she flung open the door.

The room was bathed in the soft glow of a single lamp and she felt a peculiar tightening in her chest when she saw him lying face-down on the bed. It was not the naked perfection of that long, lean body that initiated that sharp, almost painful reaction in her…it was an inexplicable recognition in her that her own body had flung itself into that same position on her own bed moments before, when hurt and desolation had threatened to overwhelm her.

Except that with him it was a case neither of hurt nor desolation, she reminded herself savagely—more likely one of temper over her having had the temerity to lie to him!

Irritated beyond all measure that he had not even appeared to have noticed her arrival, she slammed the door behind her as hard as she possibly could, then winced as she remembered the baby—the last thing she wanted was for him to waken, because she intended having her say, come what may.

He lifted his head from the pillow, his expression oddly dazed.

'Jenny…thank God you've come to your senses!'

'I've come to my senses all right,' she informed him calmly—a calm, she fatalistically accepted, that stood little or no chance of remaining with her. 'And there are a few things I intend saying to you. And, believe me, Jamie, you're going to listen, if only because it's about time someone told you a few home truths.'

She began walking towards the bed, her footsteps

never once faltering, not even when he rolled over, sat up and then propped himself up against the headrest, all with a total lack of self-consciousness and without the slightest regard to the fact that he was stark naked.

'What guarantee have I that they will be truths?' he challenged morosely, his eyes almost black with suspicion as they watched her.

'And that's all that troubles you, isn't it, Jamie?' she demanded, praying she would manage to have her say before fury finally consumed her. 'That fact that I had the gall to lie to you! The fact that I happened to have lost my virginity to you tonight is neither here nor there—of course not! The most earth-shattering event of the night was your discovering that I had committed the sacrilege of lying to you!'

'Jenny, let me—'

'*I'm* doing the talking! And I haven't finished by a long chalk!' she bellowed across his attempted words. 'Where was I? Ah, yes! The losing of my virginity…which, as even someone as amazingly insensitive as you are must surely know, is billed as being a pretty special event in the life of most women—'

'Jenny, please!' he groaned. 'Do you honestly think—?'

'You're interrupting me again, Jamie,' she informed him acidly. 'What you may not know,' she continued relentlessly, 'is that getting over the hurdle of the first time can be pretty daunting for a lot of women…which is why I—and, in retrospect, I have to admit, foolishly—selected you.'

'*Selected* me?' he roared, his expression almost comical in its outraged disbelief.

'Selected,' confirmed Jenny ruthlessly, almost beginning to enjoy the effect his words were having—and there was still more to come! 'Let's face it, Jamie, you were a pretty obvious candidate…a safe old flame. You see, I've always had this terribly inconvenient block about my first experience in lovemaking being with a man I love…I suppose I was just afraid I might do all the wrong things and put him off.' Though inwardly wincing at the sound of such drivel, she persevered. 'It's a hang-up that's played havoc with my relationships, as I'm sure you can imagine.'

He obviously couldn't; and, judging by the expression on his face, the only thing he was capable of imagining at that moment was putting his hands around her throat and throttling her.

'And now that I've met the man I want to love for the rest of my life…well…Jamie, you do understand, don't you, that I simply *had* to do something about it?'

For one fraught moment she feared she was about to dissolve into laughter at the sight of his face—a laughter she knew would rapidly deteriorate into hysteria and ruin all chance of salvaging any scrap of her pride.

'You're lying!' he raged, suddenly swinging off the bed and striding towards her. 'That ridiculous tale you just told is so riddled with flaws it's…it's nonsense!' He pulled her against him, his hand reaching down and untying her gown. 'According to your explanation of the first time—there simply wouldn't be any need of a second time…right?'

The anger in his words had dropped to a seductive whisper by the time he had finished them, and the hands impatiently removing the gown from her had grown gentle as they began coaxing and caressing her treacherously receptive body to instant reawakening.

'No!' she moaned, her hands still clenched in rejection even as her arms slid possessively around him.

'No?' he gloated softly, his lips nuzzling hers, tempting them with their passive presence until her own could endure it no longer and silenced the breathless taunt of his laughter with their hunger.

And this time, when their bodies became locked in love, it was as though they met in battle, each striving to enslave the other in its rapture, each for its own reasons determined to prove that one was lost without the other.

'Jenny, I think the only intelligent thing we can do, for the moment, is call a truce,' he gasped as they lay locked and spent in one another's arms.

He moved her against him and then, to her breathless bewilderment, began raining soft, random kisses over her face and head. They were tender kisses, the sort from which she would have wanted to cover him that first time, if only he had given her a chance. And their effect on her was to fill her with a strange mixture of hope and sadness and to bring the blur of tears to her eyes.

'So—what do you say?' he demanded lazily, repositioning her once more and nuzzling his chin against her head. 'About a truce, that is?'

'I think it's a very sensible idea,' she capitulated contentedly, placing her own series of kisses against the salty warmth of his throat and casually dismissing a mild and rather tentative suggestion from somewhere within her that she might be completely out of her mind.

For a full five minutes they were at lazy peace, his assiduous caresses, now no longer linked to the immediacy of desire, fanning that flickering spark of hope in her with their tenderness—a tenderness that was almost akin to love.

Seconds later he began eroding the truce he himself had initiated, with his probing, loaded questions. And then, moments later, his volatile temper took over and they were once more at one another's throats.

And, as before, their bitter recriminations led them

around that tortuous circle that was to become so familiar to them...when they eventually found sleep, it was
locked once more in each other's arms, their turbulent
passion yet again spent.

CHAPTER SEVEN

THE idea that she could well be out of her mind was one that surfaced in Jenny's thoughts with niggling regularity throughout her first day back at work since Jamie's return. Which wasn't surprising, she thought as she made her way home rather later than usual that evening; it had been a weekend that would have driven even the most sane of people to distraction.

Yet even now there was an irrepressible excitement within her, jostling aside her perfectly justifiable feelings of exasperation with its tingling exhilaration.

They had fought and loved and laughed throughout the entire two days and, to the amazement of them both, their tiny nephew had positively thrived on the intensely charged atmosphere between them—chuckling delightedly in accompaniment to their laughter and merely gurgling with contentment on the single occasion their voices had risen to anger in his presence.

'Perhaps he knows something we don't,' Jamie had murmured, his anger dispelled as he had taken both child and woman into his arms.

And the reason that she was undoubtedly out of her mind was that she had thrived on it too, she thought, a tinge of wariness creeping across her face as the building came into sight and she began searching in her pocket for her keys. And she was thriving solely because of that ultimately very dangerous technique she seemed to have acquired overnight—that of limiting the extent to which she was allowing her thoughts to roam.

It was the trembling of her hand as she inserted the

key in the front door lock that pulled her up with a brutal sharpness. She was blocking out far too much, she told herself in sudden panic, and facing reality was an inevitability from which there was ultimately no escape.

She pushed open the door and walked slap into Jamie, standing in the hallway with Jonathan in his arms.

'We've been watching and waiting for you for hours now,' he complained with a grin.

Before she could utter a word, he leaned over and placed a welcoming and most enthusiastic kiss on her lips. It was an action that filled her with almost equal parts of surprise and pleasure.

'We?' she murmured unsteadily, having dragged her eyes from the twinkling green of his gaze towards the baby sound asleep in the nonchalant hold of strong, darkly tanned arms.

Already her pulses were racing out of control, she realised shakily, and then wondered at her own surprise at the kiss with which he had greeted her...he was always taking her by surprise, and often with casually affectionate, completely unselfconscious gestures such as that one.

'Hey, Junior,' he growled to the oblivious baby, 'I thought the deal was that you'd stay awake for the homecoming!' His darkly fringed eyes rose for an instant, hovering on Jenny, now removing her coat, before returning to the baby. 'Though, to be fair, it was getting so late that even I was thinking of calling it a night.'

'Jamie, it's not even eight yet,' she protested, though her heart had already begun sinking with the inescapable edge that had crept into his tone. 'I told you I'd be working all hours, now that the campaign's getting under way.'

'And what about Bill—or is it Will?' he enquired, his tone now openly hostile. 'Is he working all hours too?'

'Oh, for heaven's sake!' she groaned as she hung up her coat—she was hardly through the door and already he was starting! 'Jamie, don't you think it's about time—?'

'Good idea,' he muttered, placing the sleeping baby in her arms. 'And I'll see to the food—though God only knows if it's still edible, having been ready for hours.'

'Ready for hours, my foot!' she muttered to herself as she took Jonathan to his room and tucked him into his cot. One thing she had discovered about his eating habits was that he would happily sit down to his evening meal at midnight—eight o'clock was practically mid-afternoon to him.

'Wardale—the name conjures up a picture of someone short and fat and altogether unappetising,' was his greeting the instant she joined him in the kitchen. 'What do they call him?' he continued, before she had a chance to react. 'Little Willy Wardale?'

'Well, it conjures up an entirely false picture,' retorted Jenny, wondering when on earth she would learn not to allow herself to be dragged into these futile exchanges. 'Jamie, if you don't mind, I've had rather a difficult day—I really don't feel in the mood for your juvenile humour.'

Without a glance in his direction, she took out the cutlery and began laying the kitchen table.

'It wasn't my intention to be humorous—juvenile or otherwise,' he informed her coldly. 'I was simply about to ask you how poor Willy reacted to the news.'

'To what news?' ground out Jenny with flagging patience.

'To the news that he's no longer flavour of the month.'

'For heaven's sake, Jamie—grow up, will you?' she pleaded exasperatedly, then added, in a half-hearted attempt to change the subject. 'Are we going to eat or aren't we?'

His response was to produce two plates from the warming drawer, slap an untidy helping of tagliatelle on each, over which he then proceeded to ladle dollops of sauce, before handing her one of the sauce-splattered plates.

'OK—eat!' he snarled, slamming his own plate down on the table.

Jenny sat down at the table, greatly aided in resisting the temptation to sling the lot over him by the realisation dawning on her that this grindingly oppressive behaviour of his had all the hallmarks of jealousy.

She gazed down at the mess on the plate before her, uncomfortably acknowledging the bubbling exhilaration with which the mere idea was filling her. Hating herself for her own lunacy, she picked up her fork and began eating.

Seconds later she returned the fork to the plate, choking on laughter as she swallowed what was in her mouth.

'So much for your claims to it's being ruined,' she laughed, as he gazed across at her with a blackly enquiring scowl. 'Despite the ghastly presentation, it's delicious—as usual.'

'Well enjoy it,' he growled, 'because it's the last meal I intend cooking for you until you start behaving decently.'

Jenny looked over at him, convinced she would find him grinning wickedly back at her. She let out a squeak of indignation as she was faced with the implacable coldness of his stare.

'You unspeakable hypocrite!' she gibbered. '*You* have the nerve to demand decency from *me*? What do you want—that I offer to marry you?'

'Don't be so bloody ridiculous,' he rasped scathingly.

Realising just how dangerously close she was to saying things she would probably regret for the rest of her life, Jenny rammed another forkful of food into her mouth, chewing on it with a force that would have pulverised concrete. The mere mention of marriage—even in that angry context—had certainly brought out a reaction in him, she thought bitterly. No need to ask what his reaction would have been had she really flipped— bared her soul and then got down on her knees and begged him to marry her!

'You claimed not to approve of two-timing,' he stated and, when she showed no signs of responding, continued. 'Though, as you've turned out to be something of a compulsive liar, perhaps I should discount that claim. But *I* don't happen to fancy the idea of being two-timed…so, for the time being, Willy Wardale is strictly off limits, other than in his role as your employer.'

'For the time being,' she echoed, the words a strangled squeak. 'And you, no doubt, will let me know when the time, so to speak, stops being. And how will you put it, Jamie?' she asked, her voice now quivering with rage. 'Will it be "that's it, Jenny, I've had my fill of you, so you now have my permission to get on with doing your own thing"? Or perhaps you'll dispense with words and simply install my replacement in your bed!'

His expression turned from fury to one of startled horror.

'I suppose it's pointless my asking why you have such an abysmally low opinion of me,' he muttered hoarsely.

'No—it isn't pointless; in fact, I'd be only too glad to tell you why,' she replied, pausing to choose with infinite care the words that would follow. 'I'm in the fortunate position of being able to look at our relationship with total objectivity,' she lied without a qualm.

'Really—and what puts you in such a fortunate position?' he enquired sarcastically.

'The fact that you can't hurt me,' she retorted, ruffling her fingers nervously through her hair as the thought occurred to her that she might feel better afterwards if she didn't actually count the number of lies she was about to tell. 'But I happen to have seen the hurt that you and men like you are capable of inflicting on women.'

'I hate to keep interrupting,' he murmured with a steely softness. 'But what, exactly, are men like me like?'

'Have you ever been in love, Jamie?' she asked quietly.

He gave a sharp exclamation of impatience. 'How about an answer to the question I've just asked you, before you start leaping in with ones of your own?' he snapped.

'You've never been in love, have you?' she persisted, a hollow feeling of despair chilling her.

'But you have been, haven't you, Jenny?' he retaliated harshly. 'Several times and now, finally, with Willy. You do love Willy, don't you—or was he just another of your lies?'

'Jamie, I've no idea how many romantic relationships the average man or woman has before finally settling down, but I think most people would agree that they form part of our social ritual…and that it's generally accepted that each is begun with at least some sort of chance, however small, of it developing into a lifetime commitment.'

'What you're saying is that it's only people who are looking for marriage who should enter into a relationship.'

'Jamie, I—'

'So—what about the relationship you entered into with me?' he drawled. 'You accuse me of double standards, yet you seem to find nothing wrong with using me as a means to paving the way for bliss ever after with your boss.'

'Jamie, that's—'

'It's what you claim to be the truth!' he roared across the table at her. 'And *you* have the nerve to set yourself up in judgement of *me*!' he added, leaping to his feet and flinging his napkin across the table. 'I'm seriously beginning to wonder about your ability to reason! Your only sexual experience is with me—yet you seem to think it's some sort of mechanical process that will be the same with every man you meet! And how can you possibly claim to love one man, yet make love to another in the way you do with me?'

He kicked back his chair from under him and strode off towards the door.

'And just keep your fingers crossed that the three of us never meet, because I can promise you, he'll be left in no doubt as to what sort of relationship you and I are enjoying—and I use the word "enjoying" advisedly!'

Jenny gazed down at the plate of food congealing before her. The worst part of it all was that she couldn't quarrel with a single word he had said, she thought miserably. It had been her pride that had driven her to lie—and lie to such an extent that she couldn't even face keeping a tally of them all! And now she was cornered in her own mesh of lies…and would have to come up with even more—anything, as long as it wasn't the truth.

It was a long while before she could stir herself, but once she had she rose and began clearing the table. When she had finished tidying up completely, she made a large pot of coffee. Then she found herself staring dazedly down at the pot and wondering: first why she had made it, and then how much longer Clare and Graham would be in Czechoslovakia—for that was the length of time she would have to endure this crazy, see-saw mixture of joy and despair now dominating her existence…and then wondering most of all how long she could take the unbearable strain of it all.

'I was just coming to make some coffee,' announced Jamie, strolling into the kitchen as she was preparing a tray. 'There's a yachting programme on the television after the news—I think a couple of my boats are in it. Fancy watching it?'

More than a little thrown that he had actually thought to ask her, Jenny nodded, composing her features, as nearly as she could, into an expression as coolly distant as his.

The hour-long programme featured three racing yachts, two of which were his. They were more incredibly beautiful than she could ever have imagined: graceful and delicate and seemingly far too fragile to ride the seas into which Jamie and his crew so coolly cast them.

'Was that last one the race you've just taken part in?' she asked dazedly, when the programme finally ended.

'No—that was earlier in the year,' he replied with a reminiscent smile. 'And a pretty hairy race it was too.'

Hairy, thought Jenny weakly, feeling as though she had just been wrung through a mangle—it was the most nerve-racking spectacle she had ever seen!

'Is it often that…like that?' She had almost said 'that bad' and wasn't sure what had stopped her.

'Not very often,' he replied, his eyes candidly watchful as they met hers. 'Sometimes it's worse. So perhaps you should be thanking your lucky stars that the current love of your life is in something as safe as advertising.'

'Jamie, please,' she protested wearily. 'Can't you give it a rest for a while?'

'Believe it or not, I didn't intend any sarcasm,' he informed her mildly. 'It's just that I happened to be watching your face at the point at which we almost capsized...and you didn't seem to be enjoying it.'

Jenny felt herself tense at his words, trying desperately to extract some sort of nuance from that deliberately bland tone he was employing while at the same time cringing from the thought of how much her face might have given away.

'Of course I wouldn't be happy at the thought of you or anyone else capsizing in seas like that!' she exclaimed defensively. 'You wouldn't stand much of a chance.'

'We're not a bunch of seaside trippers—we all know what we're doing.'

'I'm sure you do,' conceded Jenny. 'And I'm sure it looks far worse to the ignorant—which I most certainly am.'

He gave a sudden chuckle. 'Graham and I used to take you out now and then when you were a tiddler—I seem to remember you ending up overboard once.'

'And my mother wouldn't let me go again for years,' she laughed ruefully—remembering with a pang of guilt what a song and dance she had led her poor mother for months afterwards.

'And I suppose what you've seen tonight hasn't exactly whetted your appetite for more,' he stated in that same bland tone.

'On the contrary,' she retorted, needled by his tone, 'perhaps a bit more would teach me enough not to sit there practically chewing my fingernails to the quick the next time I watch a programme on the subject.'

'Practically chewing your fingernails to the quick, were you?' he grinned.

'Perhaps I exaggerated a little,' she said, the words coming out slightly distorted because his eyes had caught hers, trapping them and refusing to free them. 'Jamie, stop it,' she protested weakly.

'I shall if you will,' he teased lazily.

She opened her mouth to protest once more, then closed it with a sigh of defeat. She didn't want either of them to stop wanting one another like this...not ever.

'You realise, I hope, that this is likely to have the most devastating effect on my ego,' he murmured, confidence oozing from his every pore as he eased himself to his feet and sauntered over to the armchair on which she was curled, 'your using me as your plaything whenever the fancy takes you,' he finished, holding out a hand to her and pulling her to her feet.

'If your ego met a steamroller head-on, I wouldn't give anything for the steamroller's chances,' laughed Jenny. 'And anyway——'

'Shut up—or I'll not teach you to sail,' he muttered, his lips making a thorough job of ensuring she complied.

'He what?' Jenny almost shrieked, falling back weakly against the sofa.

Mandy gave her a puzzled, almost apprehensive look.

'Jenny, I'm sorry, but, the way Jamie spoke, I assumed you knew. He simply said he was off to Rio again.'

'For heaven's sake, Mandy, of course I didn't know!' exclaimed Jenny exasperatedly, then immediately gave a groan of contrition. 'I'm sorry, Mandy—I didn't mean to take it out on you,' she apologised. 'It's just that I'd hate to think you could believe I'd knowingly leave you in the lurch until this hour.' She checked her watch, her face creasing in horror. 'It's almost half-past eight—for heaven's sake, Mandy, you've been here almost twelve hours!'

Mandy smiled, shrugging dismissively. 'Looking after

Jonathan isn't exactly hard labour—and besides, I didn't have anything planned for tonight.'

'But you easily could have,' protested Jenny indignantly, her mind then recoiling in horror as the question of all the other evenings lying ahead suddenly occurred to her.

'Jenny, I was about to make some tea when you arrived,' said Mandy placatingly. 'So why don't you get out of those wet things while I make it?'

Jenny glanced down at her soaked raincoat.

'How could he possible *do* this?' she groaned in dazed disbelief.

'Jenny, it's pointless getting yourself in a state over it,' pointed out Mandy gently. 'So—off with your wet things, while I see to the tea.'

'Naturally you'll be paid for all the extra hours you've worked today, but you should also have time off for them as well,' fretted Jenny as the two of them later shared a pot of tea. 'I know Clare will insist on it…but unfortunately at the moment I can't take time off work to let you have it.'

'That's very generous—but it's also something you shouldn't be worrying about right now,' protested Mandy. 'Our most important consideration is getting something worked out for the evenings. I'm not sure if I could stay this late every night, but—'

'Mandy, I wouldn't dream of asking you to even if you could!' gasped Jenny.

'But you obviously work long hours.'

'Only when we're slap bang in the middle of a hectic period—such as right now,' explained Jenny, fury welling in her. 'And it's only likely to last a couple of weeks…which Jamie knew, damn him!'

'I could manage until seven, if that would help,' offered Mandy.

'Help?' groaned Jenny. 'Mandy, I wouldn't know how to begin thanking you! I—' She broke off, their eyes meeting in alarm as a long roll of thunder split the air.

Jenny rose to her feet and went to the window.

'It's bucketing down!' she exclaimed. 'I can call you a taxi—or you're welcome to spend the night.'

'I suppose I might as well stay,' chuckled Mandy. 'But I'd better give my flatmate a ring.'

When Mandy had made her call and then, on her own insistence, had gone off to make herself up one of the beds in Jonathan's room, Jenny went to the kitchen to make them some supper.

She was astounded by the serenity with which Mandy was taking it all—as though it really hadn't ruffled her in the least! And it probably hadn't ruffled Mandy in the least, she suddenly realised—simply because Mandy was taking it in the way any normal, self-composed person would…it was she who was carrying on as though it were a major catastrophe.

She began slowing down her movements as she prepared the food, attempting to calm herself. Jamie, for reasons he would no doubt soon be ringing her to explain, had had to return to Brazil, she reasoned with herself. Oh, yes? The simplest thing in the world would have been for him to pick up the phone and ring her at work…or to leave her a note!

'My, that smells delicious!' exclaimed Mandy, joining her in the kitchen.

Jenny gazed down at the food she had been reheating with all the interest of an automaton.

'I'm afraid it's the left-overs of something Jamie made last night.' Two plates of which she had thrown away barely touched, she remembered, her thoughts suddenly veering, not towards the blazing row that had led to the food being wasted, but to the passion they had shared throughout the night. 'I hope it takes kindly to reheating,' she added, momentarily closing her eyes in a desperate attempt to block out the searing vividness of the memories assaulting her.

'Good heavens—so he can cook too!' laughed Mandy. 'I couldn't believe my eyes when I saw that television documentary featuring him last night—I'd no idea he was so famous.'

'Yes…I suppose he is famous,' said Jenny and then became aware of the slightly puzzled look her remark elicited from Mandy. 'It's just that I've known him since I was a child,' she offered by way of explanation. 'You tend not to think of people that familiar to you as famous.'

'I suppose not,' said Mandy, her tone a little uncertain, then she opened a drawer and took out the cutlery. 'Jenny, I…when I first met Jamie I was…heck, I might as well be honest, I probably drooled like an idiot! You don't often come across men who look like him…unless it's on a cinema or television screen!'

Jenny gave a sympathetic smile as she served up the food and took it to the table.

'I shouldn't worry about it—that's the way most women tend to react to him.' And more or less the way she herself had been reacting to him for the best part of her life, she reminded herself bitterly.

'But the thing I find most amazing about him,' enthused Mandy, 'is the way he managed to make it crystal-clear he wasn't available, without actually coming out with the words and without hurting my feelings in the slightest.' She pulled a rueful face as she sat down. 'You know, I still haven't been able to work out exactly how he accomplished it—but all I can say is that it was done with brilliance and the utmost tact.'

Jenny sat down at the table, having to compose her

face into a bland mask while her mind contended with
the thought that tact was one attribute she would never
in a million years have ascribed to Jamie.

'And I'd really like to apologise for the way I behaved,' Mandy was continuing. 'I honestly didn't mean
any harm—'

'Mandy,' interrupted Jenny with a protesting laugh.
'Before you really start getting carried away—I think I
should point out that Jamie and I aren't...well, aren't
what you appear to think we are. I thought you realised
what our relationship is,' she battled on a trifle disjointedly, an irrational part of her feeling almost as though
she were denying her own existence. 'Clare—his sister,
in case you hadn't realised—is married to my brother.'

'Yes, I know, but...I felt that...oh heck, why don't I
just shut up?'

Jamie neither rang nor wrote.

On the third day after his departure—a Friday—
Mandy didn't turn up at the flat.

After having waited the best part of an hour, to allow
for such contingencies as traffic problems, Jenny was
beginning to feel decidedly concerned by the time the
telephone eventually rang.

'Jenny, it's taken me until now to muster up enough
of a voice to be able to call you,' croaked Mandy barely
intelligibly.

'Mandy, you sound ghastly, love,' gasped Jenny.
'What's wrong?'

'I woke up feeling like absolute death—and completely out of the blue,' rasped Mandy miserably. 'I suppose it's flu—there's a lot of it around.'

'Well, don't you try to do any more talking—it must
be agony. And get yourself back to bed.'

'But what about you and Jonathan—and your campaign?' wailed Mandy, sounding almost on the verge of tears.

'Mandy, we're only at the preliminary stages of the campaign,' soothed Jenny—that ghastly period when there just weren't enough hours in a day, she reminded herself with a twinge of panic. 'And as for Jonathan, if Jamie hasn't turned up by Monday, I'll simply take him to the office…I've done it before.' She rolled her eyes heavenwards as she uttered those words, then gave a fatalistic shrug.

'That's a relief—I was so worried I'd be putting you in a very awkward position,' said Mandy, her voice now a ravaged whisper. 'I suppose you've still not heard from Jamie.'

'Jamie? Jamie who?' joked Jenny, forcing a chuckle into her words. 'Now, just you get yourself back to bed, my girl, and stay there until you're completely better,' she bullied affectionately. 'Would you like me to ring your doctor?'

'No, I'll do that—he'll be round like a shot when he hears me croaking like this. And I'll definitely wait till I'm over this before coming back to work—this is the last thing either you or Jonathan need.'

'You'll have no voice left if you carry on talking like this, so off you go!' protested Jenny. 'And you take care of yourself, Mandy—promise?'

It took Jenny a good ten minutes to compose herself sufficiently to ring Ellie.

'I realise this couldn't possibly have come at a worse time,' she said, having explained her predicament. 'And I know that— '

'Take it easy, Jenny,' cut in Ellie with a soothing chuckle. 'This couldn't actually have happened on a better day, believe it or not. The artwork that was going to keep us going flat-out today hasn't turned up—there's been some hitch or other with it.'

'Ellie—are you serious?' exclaimed Jenny. 'I can't believe it!'

'There's more—Gil won't be in either; he rang his secretary first thing…perhaps he's got a dose of the same flu your nanny's got,' chuckled Ellie. 'So there's nothing to stop you having a nice relaxed day at home with the baby!'

'Today, yes—but what about Monday?' fretted Jenny. 'Mandy certainly won't be fit by then and if Jamie doesn't show up over the weekend—'

'If Jamie doesn't show up then I admit there could be problems,' agreed Ellie briskly. 'But it won't do you any good worrying over such an eventuality before you really have to—meanwhile we'll all be keeping our fingers crossed for you here.'

It was only once she had replaced the receiver that Jenny realised how impossible it would be for her to follow Ellie's well-intentioned advice…how could she? If Jamie didn't turn up she might just as well say goodbye to her job.

CHAPTER EIGHT

'JENNY, I was expecting you to come and have a talk with me before you finally left,' stated Gil Wardale, managing to sound more than a little put out.

Jenny carried the telephone over to an armchair and sat down. Why wouldn't he leave well enough alone? she wondered wearily; she had tendered her resignation and he had accepted it and that, as far as she was concerned, was that.

'Gil, I really didn't feel there was anything more to be discussed. I realise you must feel I've let you all down appallingly, but I honestly felt it was fairer to do so then, rather than risking having to do so next week when the campaign is properly under way. Gil, I know it'll be nightmarish for you trying to find a replacement—'

'We've already got one,' he cut in. 'One of the others on the short-list with you fortunately still happened to be free.'

So much for her tentative fear that they might have found her difficult to replace, thought Jenny wryly.

'But that's not why I rang,' he continued. 'One of the things I wanted to mention was accommodation—not that anything's come up regarding those two properties I mentioned, but I thought I'd check if you're still interested.'

'To be honest, I hadn't given it much thought recently,' replied Jenny dazedly—this man had a knack of confounding her with his strange switches from insensitivity to concern.

'But you'll still be needing somewhere to live shortly, won't you? Or have your plans changed?'

'No...I mean—yes, I shall be needing somewhere,' she stammered. In fact, she would be needing somewhere the instant Jonathan was reunited with his parents!

'Good—I'll continue to keep an ear open, then,' said Gil, sounding vaguely relieved. 'Another thing I wanted to mention—and this is a very long shot—I'm opening up an office in Australia—Sydney, to be exact—in a few months. If the other side of the world should by any chance appeal to you, there would be a job there for you.'

Jenny glanced down in bemusement at the receiver in her hand, convinced she must have misheard.

'As I said—it was very much a long shot,' muttered Gil. 'The reason I make the offer is that I have a good eye for talent—and I spotted quite a bit of it in what little I saw of your work here.'

'I'd have thought talent was pretty useless unless it was backed up by reliability,' pointed out Jenny, the bitterness within her rising without warning to the surface.

'It wasn't a question of unreliability,' contradicted Gil. 'You found yourself in an abnormal spot and did what you had to do, given the circumstances...just as I did what I had to do. Jenny, we both know that yours wasn't the sort of job that could have been kept open in the hope that circumstances would right themselves. It was your professionalism that prompted your resignation and mine that forced me to accept it. And the Australian offer, for what it's worth, isn't an empty one. I have no idea how such a career change would affect your personal life...but I'd like to think it's an offer you would at least consider.'

'It's one I'm most tempted to consider,' blurted out

Jenny…Australia, being half a world away, was suddenly the most attractive of places!

'Give in to the temptation,' urged Gil, with an uncharacteristically light-hearted laugh. 'And, in the meantime, I'll be in touch if anything definite crops up regarding accommodation.'

Halfway through those words, Jenny had begun losing track of them; her attention becoming riveted by the sound of a key in the front door. By the time she had replaced the receiver she was trembling with a debilitating mixture of anger and apprehension.

'Hello there, Mandy, I—' Jamie's words, uttered as he strolled into the room, came to an abrupt halt as he spotted Jenny.

Her hand still resting on the telephone, Jenny felt as though she was being bombarded by his presence. It was as though she had forgotten the size of him; the rugged sharpness of his features, the stubbled darkness that shadowed his face when he needed a shave, as he obviously did now, and the golden richness of his tan, accentuated even more so now by the pale, almost white, of the raincoat encasing the broad planes of his shoulders.

And as she looked, the anger in her exacerbated by the treacherous excitement pulsing through her, she saw his eyes narrow and their surprise replaced by a look that was disconcertingly close to contempt.

'Oh, it's you—where's Mandy?'

Jenny felt herself stiffen from the shock of those words, then freeze to rigidity at the unexpected sound of her own reply.

'Terribly sorry to disappoint you, darling,' she drawled, astounding herself by the fact that she hadn't yet given in to a powerful urge to attack him physically—and with any and every weapon that happened to come to hand. 'But, as you see, it's just little old me here.'

His eyes swept slowly down, then back up, her body, desire igniting with swift and powerful spontaneity in their depths as they made their leisurely journey.

'Have there been any calls for me?' he demanded, his cold tone denying the heat he had been unable to suppress in his eyes.

'Any calls for you?' murmured Jenny, hating both herself and him for the feeling of intoxicated excitement that glimpse of desire had awakened in her. 'Now—let me see.' For God's sake, she demanded of herself in outraged disbelief, what was she playing at? She was face to face with the man whose casual lack of concern for anyone other than himself had put paid to what had once been her dream job!

'Cut it out, will you?' he rasped impatiently. 'I'm in no mood—'

'*You're* in no mood!' she exploded, her hands clenching till she could feel the sting of her nails biting into her flesh. 'That's all that matters to you, isn't it, Jamie?' she let fly with growing hysteria. 'What you're in the mood for is all that counts—and to hell with the rest of the world!'

'Do you mind not screeching liked that?' he muttered disdainfully, shrugging out of his raincoat. 'You'll terrify the baby.'

'The baby?' she shrieked even louder. 'My God— don't tell me you've suddenly remembered his existence! Our nephew, that child for which you and I share joint responsibility—or so you conned me into believing!'

'For God's sake, pull yourself together,' he snapped, turning from her in disgust and striding from the room.

'Don't you dare walk out on me like that!' raged

Jenny, tearing after him. 'I've things to say to you, Jamie Castile, and you're damned well going to hear every one of them!'

'I'm all ears,' he drawled, opening the door of the baby's room and entering. 'But you can stop screaming—I'm not deaf.'

He walked across to the cot and lifted out the wide-awake, cooing baby, seating himself on the edge of one of the beds and suddenly lifting the infant high above his head.

'Did you miss your bad Uncle Jamie?' he demanded, laughing up at the baby now squealing with delight. 'Stop dribbling all over me and answer,' chuckled Jamie. 'I'm sure a lad as clever as you has heard how to hold a decent conversation by now.'

Jenny stood by the door, the seething rage within her exacerbated by the onset of a disgustingly gooey melting sensation attacking her in the pit of her stomach.

It was all very well for him doing the doting uncle routine, she told herself savagely as she strode purposefully into the room, but the fact was, he was an irresponsible monster!

'There's no depth to which you're not prepared to sink, is there, Jamie?' she accused scathingly. 'And if you think that stooping to using Jonathan as a shield is going to protect you from what I have to say, you can think again!'

'What a twisted little mind you have, Jennifer,' he drawled. 'But don't let us interrupt you—just carry on ranting.'

Certain she would have physically attacked him had he not been holding their nephew, Jenny walked to the window, anger and frustration welling hopelessly in her as she found her view impaired by the blur of angry tears filling her eyes.

'I don't know why,' she began hoarsely, 'but I trusted you.'

'A loaded statement, if ever I heard one,' he observed, his tone verging on boredom.

'You actually managed to sound sincere when you talked about the importance of the work Clare and Graham are doing...and how you and I were duty-bound to do all we could to help ease their concern over Jonathan. But you never had any intention of pulling your weight, did you, Jamie?'

'Who am I to question the word of the oracle?' he drawled, his words almost drowned by the shrieks of delight coming from the baby. 'But I'd prefer it if you dispensed with all this heavy innuendo and came to the point...I take it all these histrionics are in some way connected with my temporary absence.'

'Your temporary absence,' echoed Jenny witheringly. 'I suppose you wouldn't have been in the least aggrieved had I disappeared, without so much as a word of warning, for well over a week—and also without so much as a single telephone call during the entire time?'

'You can drop the martyred tone—it's beginning to grate,' he snapped. 'Damn it, you know perfectly well I have a business to run, one that happens to take me a lot further afield than yours does.'

'Oh, you do actually remember that I too have a career to consider, do you?' she exclaimed frigidly. 'Nothing as glamorous or as lucrative as yours, but one I had pride in and enjoyed—'

'Oh, for God's sake!' he exclaimed impatiently. 'Stop droning on about your damned career—the only thing you missed out on was a baby-sitter! But all your night-life was here with me...perhaps it's that you were missing—'

'You are utterly despicable!' she rounded on him, her

face white with anger. 'And, what's more, you knew
perfectly well I'd be working late during that precise
period in which you chose to disappear!'

'You couldn't possibly have had to work late *every*
night,' he retorted. 'And I'm sure Mandy would have
been only too willing to...' He broke off. 'Where *is*
Mandy?'

Shaking with barely suppressed rage, Jenny strode towards him.

'That's one of the many things you would already
know had you troubled to ring even once during your
absence,' she informed him icily.

He lowered the baby on to his lap, his eyes suspicious
as he gazed up at her.

'Spit it out, Jenny—where is she?'

'Mandy's at home—recuperating.'

'Recuperating? What the hell's that supposed to
mean?'

'Precisely what it says. She's recuperating from the
particularly bad bout of flu she went down with a few
days after you took off!' A bout of flu which, for several
terrifying days, she had been convinced Jonathan too
showed signs of having caught, she reminded herself bitterly.

His gaze moved from her to the baby on his knee.

'Awkward,' he conceded, with no discernible trace of
remorse. 'But I'm sure you didn't have too many problems getting time off—you being so close to the boss.'

Awkward? thought Jenny, too incensed to be capable
of putting her murderous reaction into words. Oh, yes,
it had certainly been most awkward! And no, she had
had no problem getting time off work—because she had
simply had no choice other than to take it! There had
been other moments he might also have chosen to describe as awkward, she thought with mounting bitter-

ness—such as the series of heated exchanges she had
had with the doctor she had kept calling out to Jonathan
in those couple of days of near panic when she was
convinced he was showing flu symptoms. When her tiny
charge had finally produced the tooth the doctor was
convinced was the cause of his fretfulness, she had been
too relieved even to feel a twinge of humiliation over
unreasonable behaviour. And relief, too, had been her
only discernible feeling when she had, a day later, taken
the only decision open to her and resigned from Wardale's.

'Jenny, you don't seem to have been listening,' he
goaded softly. 'I said—'

'I *heard* what you said,' she retorted angrily; yet even
as her eyes poured their scorn into his she found herself
caught in the mind-shattering paradox of loving him
with as much fervour as she loathed him.

And the unspeakable fact was that she did still love
him, she thought despairingly. Despite his careless indifference to the mayhem his actions could have—indeed had—wrought on her life…she still loved him with
that same mindless intensity. Loving him had been a
disease which had lasted throughout her formative years
and which had lasted on to plague her still. But she was
damned if she was going to allow herself to be subjected
to so destructive a love forever, she vowed, her chin
lifting in defiance as she reached out for the baby.

'It's time I bathed and fed him,' she stated, emitting
an exclamation of exasperation as he drew both himself
and the child back from her.

'Why the sudden rush, Jenny?' he drawled uncooperatively, a blank coldness in his eyes.

'I told you—it's time I fed and bathed him,' she repeated woodenly, battling to keep control of herself.

'I'm sure he can wait until you've got all those things

you had to say to me off your chest,' he murmured infuriatingly.

'I've finished saying what I had to say,' she snapped,
her words driving it home to her that she had said precisely nothing—that everything she had intended throw-
ing at him was still bottled up within her. 'So now I'd
like to get on with seeing to Jonathan.'

His response was to draw even further back from her
outstretched arms, cradling the baby to him.

'A thought has just occurred to me,' he announced
conversationally.

'Perhaps you'd like to examine it undisturbed while I
get on with bathing Jonathan,' hissed Jenny from between clenched teeth. Not until she had the baby bathed,
fed and asleep would she be in a position to speak her
mind and in the manner in which she intended.

'The way I see it, if you've done the intelligent thing
and followed my advice,' he continued stubbornly, 'that
is, given Wardale his marching orders—'

'My God, I can hardly believe I'm hearing this!'
gasped Jenny. 'You swan off for days at a stretch—you
don't even have the common politeness to pick up a
phone and explain yourself—and when you do decide to
swan back you ask me if I've carried out your damned
orders! Give me that child and let me get out of here
before I really start telling you what I think of you!'

'*I'll* bathe him,' stated Jamie, avoiding her by swinging over to the other side of the bed and on to his feet.
'You're obviously in no fit state to be doing anything
with him.'

Speechless with rage, Jenny tried to string together a
coherent sentence. After only a couple of seconds she
gave up the struggle, turned on her heel and marched
off to the kitchen.

It was like some appalling farce, she told herself

dazedly as she set about preparing the baby's supper. How dared he? His taking off like that had just about wrecked her career—and, whatever Gil might say about her professionalism, her failure with Wardale's was an indelible blot on her record…yet when he had deigned to turn up again he had managed to tie her up in mental knots to such an extent that she had been incapable of letting him know exactly what his irresponsible actions had cost her. And to crown it all, he had just implied she wasn't fit to take care of Jonathan!

'You seem to have misinterpreted my reference to Wardale earlier,' he stated without preamble, when he later joined her in the kitchen with the bathed and cherubically contented baby in his arms. 'Quite frankly, whether you see him or not is no longer of any interest to me.'

His words hit her with the force of a violent blow. She had once asked him how it would end between them, she thought with a sickening shudder, and now she knew.

'So why did you even bother to mention him?' she demanded with a brittle iciness, the memory awakening in her of the unmistakable need that had leapt unguarded into his eyes as they had swept over her.

'Because it occurred to me that, had you severed your…' he paused, as though savouring the scorn with which he was to lace his following words '…your romantic ties with Wardale, he might have got nasty and used your asking for time off as an excuse to turf you out of your job. I seem to remember you saying you were still on probation with his company.'

'I did,' stated Jenny, her thoughts crashing into one another in jumbled confusion. 'In fact, your judgement of the situation is way off course,' she blurted out, driven by a pride that was stridently demanding it be protected at all costs. 'You see, Gil and I have decided that because of the...the seriousness of our relationship, it's better that I no longer work for his company.'

The moment she had finished speaking she was wondering how on earth she could possibly have come out with such a load of complete drivel. The fact that she had fallen into the trap of adding yet more lies to the seemingly interminable list she had already already told him was the least of her worries—what incensed and frustrated her beyond measure was the realisation that she had deprived herself of the satisfaction of informing him of exactly how much his cavalier behaviour had cost her!

It was Jamie who fed the baby and settled him down to sleep—all without having uttered a single further word to Jenny, who occupied herself by performing small, useless tasks in the kitchen with all the awareness of a zombie.

What she was now finding almost impossible to believe was the ease with which she had landed herself even deeper into a morass of lies, from which there could be no extracting herself without suffering total humiliation.

Completely lost in her unpalatable thoughts, she let out a shriek of fright when she was suddenly grasped by the arm.

'Right—now we start talking,' announced Jamie, dragging her by her captured arm into the living room. 'Sit down,' he ordered, ensuring she obeyed by shoving her forcefully back on to the sofa.

'If you think—'

'This sudden change in your relationship with Wardale,' he interrupted with a snarl. 'Am I to understand that you and he have become lovers during my absence?'

'That's none of your damned business!'

'Oh, but it is,' he informed her softly, his eyes bright chips of ice as he towered menacingly above her. 'I won't stand for you sharing another man's bed while you're still sharing mine.'

'Is that so?' she demanded with savage fury. 'Because I have news for you, Jamie—I've no intention of sharing your damned bed again! And what happened to your earlier claim that you couldn't care less whether I saw Gil or not?'

'*Saw* him—precisely!' he bellowed down at her. 'I made no mention of sleeping with him!'

'You hypocrite! You're nothing but a dog in the manger!' she howled back at him, almost beside herself with fury. 'Why can't you just be honest and admit it? You'd decided you'd had enough of me until you got it into your head I was sleeping with someone else!'

'Are you telling me you're not?' he demanded, reaching down and jerking her to her feet.

'No, I'm not!' she raged, lashing out wildly in an effort to escape him.

'And which of us isn't being honest now?' he snarled, his arms entrapping her flailing body like bands of steel. 'I warned you, Jenny,' he growled, pulling her against the angry tautness of his body. 'I warned you it could never be the same with him as it was for us.'

'You were wrong,' she cried out as his lips impatiently sought hers. 'You were wrong,' she continued protesting, even though her body had already begun welcoming his with a blatant, trembling hunger.

'If I was so wrong, why do you still want me as much as I want you?' he accused, his mouth punishing hers, his hands swift and impatient as they stripped the clothes from her openly acquiescent body.

And her hands were as impatient as his, revelling in

the familiar muscled contours they had so missed, blatant in their trembling joy as they caressed and explored. Yet, even as their bodies fused in an almost violent intensity of need, there still poured from him a barrage of barely coherent accusation, lashing into her until she cried out in protest against it.

And suddenly he heeded her cries, anger no longer tainting his passion as his body seemed to recognise and accept the love with which it was being bombarded. And then it was she who was berating him with softly sobbed cries of love as passion soared and peaked between them, then pinnacled and exploded with a force that left them spent and incapable of any words.

She fell asleep in the sanctuary of his arms—a sanctuary which, though she knew it to be false, was all she had. And she awoke later alone, still on the tasselled softness of the rug on which they had made love, but now with the quilt from her bed draped around her.

'I've made a pot of coffee.'

Jenny raised herself up on her elbows, the love-bruised tenderness of her body bombarding her with memories as she turned towards where those quietly spoken words had come from. He was seated on the sofa, an unbelted dressing-gown covering the darkly tanned breadth of his shoulders, his long legs clad in pyjama bottoms, the top half of which lay beside him on the sofa.

Jenny found herself unable to speak, her words constricted by a feeling of self-conscious awkwardness she had never before experienced in the aftermath of their loving.

'Here, take this,' he said, picking up the pyjama jacket and tossing it over to her.

The heavy silk of the material offered her no warmth as she slipped into the top, and she was aware of her hands shaking as though from a terrible cold as they fumbled to do up the buttons.

'Well—would you like some of this coffee or not?' he asked, impatience edging into his tone as he leaned forward to the tray on the table before him.

'I'd like some—thank you,' managed Jenny, sitting up fully and hugging the quilt around her.

She watched in silence as he poured the coffee, envying the confident ease of his movements and wondering at her own feelings of self-conscious awkwardness. And then she was no longer wondering, but seeing things as they were; understanding that her own mind had reached a point of saturation with all the lies and deceit and knowing that, if only for the sake of her own integrity, she would have to admit all that she had been guilty of unless she was to end up lying her true self out of all existence.

'Thank you,' she said, accepting the coffee he reached over to hand her, and took a deep breath. 'Jamie, I—' She broke off with a groaned mixture of disbelief and frustration as the telephone rang and he immediately reached over to answer it.

She raised the cup to her lips, willing herself to maintain the purpose to continue where she had been interrupted once he had finished. She *would* have her say, she vowed silently to herself, praying his conversation would end before her resolution deserted her.

'Thank God for that! It was a fiasco we could well have done without... And the boat? Good! No, leave all that, Mark, and we'll sort it out when you get back.' The receiver wedged to his ear between his cheek and shoulder, he reached for his cup and began drinking from it. 'No, of course not...I'm only sorry I had to leave when I did... No, but the police were bound to back down once they came to their senses.'

Jenny's eyes widened in puzzlement as she heard those words.

'And the Australians? Hell, that bad?' he muttered, frowning.

There was another prolonged silence as he listened, his eyes flickering towards Jenny, yet barely seeming to see her before they moved away and he began speaking again.

'OK, give them what help you can, but I want you and the rest of the guys to get yourselves and the boat packed up and out of there—and that's an order!' He gave a chuckle. 'We've wasted enough time as it is over this little lot!'

He replaced the receiver, then went over to a white-wood cabinet in a corner of the room and poured himself a drink.

'Would you care to join me?' he asked, raising a whisky tumbler towards her.

'No—I shan't, thanks,' replied Jenny quietly. 'I take it you have something to celebrate.'

He remained where he was, his expression brooding as he gazed down into the glass in his hand.

'What makes you think that?' he enquired coldly before draining the glass.

'I...I don't know...I'm sorry,' stammered Jenny, the oddness of his behaviour only exacerbating her nervousness and apprehension.

'Sorry?' he challenged tauntingly, refilling his glass and returning to the sofa. 'Who for—me?'

'No! Certainly not for you!' she exclaimed hotly, her temper snapping. 'You're the last person anyone with any intelligence would feel sorry for! It's simply that I gathered from your conversation that something had happened to your boat!'

'Oh, I see—it's the boat you feel sorry for,' he

drawled, then added, almost as though to himself,
'Though I suppose the poor old girl could do with a bit
of sympathy.'

'It was damaged?'

He nodded.

'And that was why you had to return to Brazil?'
probed Jenny, her memories of his reticence that first
time he had returned from Brazil, and where her leaping
to conclusions had then landed her, acting as a momen-
tary curb on her temper…not that she even remotely
believed that he could come up with anything that could
excuse his behaviour this time.

'One of the Australian boats got into difficulties and
slammed into ours.' His eyes were glacial as they met
hers; disconcertingly so, given how passionately she
knew he felt about his boats. 'The collision unfortunately
caused our boat to land virtually on top of a small police
cutter that just happened to be passing. All three boats
ended up the worse for wear…and both racing crews in
gaol.'

'In gaol—how dreadful!' gasped Jenny.

He gave a small shrug that seemed to imply indifference.

'It wasn't that dreadful. The police didn't take long to
come down from their high horses and release them—it
was an obvious accident and they had simply over-
reacted. What was inconvenient, not to say worrying,
was having a valuable prototype racing yacht in need of
repairs so far from our own boat-yard.'

'You must have been extremely worried!' exclaimed
Jenny, and immediately hated herself for having offered
him so transparent an opportunity to excuse himself for
not having contacted her…and, no matter what he might
say, there just *wasn't* any excuse!

'Of course I was damned well worried,' he snapped irritably.

'So worried that you were incapable of picking up a telephone and explaining your absence?' she demanded frigidly—he obviously wasn't interested in easy options.

'No—I wasn't that worried,' he replied, a glittering hardness in the eyes that met hers. 'I could so easily have rung you.'

'But you didn't.'

'But I didn't,' he echoed with chilling bitterness. 'It's a small world, isn't it, Jenny? A disconcertingly, almost ridiculously small world.'

Her eyes rose to his in complete bemusement, but his were trained on the glass in his hand.

'I met an Australian lawyer on the flight out to Rio,' he suddenly continued. 'As people do on such long and boring flights, we got talking.' He broke off to take a sip from his glass, turning it in his hands and examining it minutely before continuing. 'Oddly enough, his reason for going to Rio was linked to mine—the skipper of the Australian boat was a close friend of his and he'd heard there had been some trouble with the police. Being a good friend, and also having planned to visit Rio anyway, he thought he'd rearrange his itinerary. Did I mention, by the way, that he was on a three-month globe-trotting holiday?'

Jenny shook her head, not that she felt he was seeking any reply from her.

'Well, he was…and one of the places he'd visited was London—where he'd been staying with his sister and her husband.'

She found her eyes locked on those strong, tanned fingers encircling the whisky tumbler and wondering where on earth this rambling tale could possibly be leading.

'He was worried about his sister's marriage—he was obviously very fond of her and rather protective. He saw the problem as being the fact that the husband was a workaholic—a real high-flyer who had made quite a name for himself.' He drained his glass, rising to his feet as he did so. 'I dare say he's right and the guy is a workaholic...but I didn't reckon that to be the worst of her problems—not when her husband happens to be one Gil Wardale of glitzy advertising fame!'

CHAPTER NINE

JENNY remained huddled in stunned confusion on the floor, oblivious of Jamie's leaving, her mind recoiling in horror as she digested the words he had just uttered and began to understand exactly how she must appear in his eyes.

Her movements leaden, she rose to her feet, picking up the quilt and hugging it around her in a vain search for warmth.

She had been about to tell him the truth, she reasoned with herself, and now she had even more reason to go ahead and do so. But it wasn't until after she had dawdled over showering herself and was belted into the fleecy warmth of a dressing-gown that she finally found the courage to go looking for him.

Finding him in none of the other rooms, she eventually found herself outside his bedroom, the deep breath she took in an attempt to steady herself catching chokingly in the back of her throat as she knocked and then immediately entered.

The first thing that hit her was the icy chill in the air, then she saw him standing gazing out of the wide-open window.

'Jamie, I need to talk to you,' she began, a sickening sense of foreboding suddenly filling her.

She paused, waiting for some sign of acknowledgement from him, the feeling within her almost choking her when he gave none and she walked to where he stood and felt the harsh chill of the night air enfold her.

'Jamie...I seem to have got myself into the most ap-

palling mess,' she struggled on in a voice tight with tension.

'Just tell me yes or no—did you know he was married?' he asked, the matter-of-fact calm of his tone only
increasing her confusion.

'Jamie, it's not quite as simple as that; I—'

'Oh, yes, it is, sweetie-pie,' he drawled, slamming
shut the window and drawing the curtains before turning
to her with a smile that was coldly saturnine. 'You said
something just now about seeming to have got yourself
into an appalling mess. But I very much wonder whether
"seem" comes into it at all. You see, I've always had
considerable difficulty coming to grips with your unbridled enthusiasm for making love with me while still
claiming to be in love with another man. But suddenly
I'm beginning to get the picture...and, believe me, it's
not a particularly pretty one.'

'Jamie, I—'

'You what, Jenny?' he drawled. 'You're not in love
with him? No—I don't believe for one moment that you
are. But you've obviously singled out this man as the
one for you. What's his special attraction, Jenny? It can't
simply be his money. Perhaps it's his success—or perhaps you're turned on by the power you feel he wields.
Perhaps it's a combination of all those things, plus the
fact that he's a workaholic who'll leave you with plenty
of time to get your sexual kicks with the likes of me.'

'For God's sake, Jamie, what are you saying?'
croaked Jenny, slumping weakly against the wall.

'What am I saying?' he mimicked savagely. 'I'm
merely painting you a verbal picture of what I see. Of a
woman so calculating that she decided to cut her sexual
teeth, not on her intended victim, but on some other
sucker. But it paid off, didn't it? And now your relationship with this married victim of yours has become

so—what was the word you used?—serious that he can no longer bear the idea of you having to work for your living. What's the plan, Jenny—will he set you up in a love-nest until he gets rid of that unfortunate appendage: his wife?' He broke off, theatrically clutching his hand to his head. 'Silly me! That's probably one of his main attractions—the fact that he's married! There are some of us who simply balk at the idea of committing ourselves to something as final as marriage...or perhaps it's simply that you have a spot of future blackmail in mind.'

It was then that she hit him—and did so with every ounce of strength she possessed. But he was laughing as he involuntarily raised a hand to the cheek against which hers had stung, and laughing still as his other hand snaked out and trapped her by the nape of her neck.

'Your trouble is that you didn't allow for my turning up and disrupting all those plans of yours,' he taunted softly. 'And you and I aren't finished with one another yet, not by a long way.'

'Jamie, please...stop this,' she begged. 'All I ask is a chance to—'

'I'm not prepared to give you any chances,' he laughed, pulling her against him. 'The only time you and I have left is until Clare and Graham collect Jonathan. I don't know how long that will be...but we'll just have to make sure it's enough.'

'Enough for what?' she croaked, her head swimming sickeningly.

'For you to learn exactly what that sexy little body of yours is capable of between the sheets.'

'Jamie...don't...please,' she protested weakly as his arms began sliding seductively around her.

'Don't?' he enquired with mocking surprise. 'You came to me to learn, didn't you? Now I intend teaching you what it's all really about.'

'It's supposed to be about love!' she blurted out in sudden panic, terrified by the cold purposefulness now in him.

'Love?' he demanded harshly, his hands beginning their mesmerisingly gentle assault on her body. 'Perhaps that is what it's supposed to be about—but not for us, eh, Jenny? It's a disease I've been successful in avoiding so far and one that you also seem hell-bent on avoiding.'

'I'm not, I—' Her words gasped to a halt as he pulled her from him, his expression malevolent.

'Ah—so you've no objections to being loved, in fact; that's part of the deal, is it? Just so long as you're not required to love in return? Well, I hate to disappoint you, darling, but love has never been part of any deal with me. You're out of my life the instant the baby is—and don't you ever forget that!' He gave a soft, humourless laugh, then drew her back into his arms, a persuasive huskiness entering his tone as he lowered his head to hers. 'But you and I have so much to experience between then and now.'

Jenny peeked into the pram and stroked the soft cheek of her nephew lying there in wakeful contentment. Placing a brimming mug of coffee on a coaster on the table, she flung herself down on the sofa, her eyes closing automatically.

Today she had almost been tempted to ask Mrs Lodge to keep an eye on Jonathan while she caught up on sleep...now that the unfriendly, monosyllabic housekeeper had gone she was glad she had resisted the temptation. She pulled a wry face as she remembered her relief when the woman had first turned up—presumably on the day Jamie had originally been due back from Brazil—and remembered how quickly she had returned to praying for Mandy's speedy recovery and return. The very idea of Mrs Lodge offering to do her—or anyone else, for that matter—a favour, now struck her as humorous…Mrs Lodge did her daily four-hour stint, plus the shopping Jamie asked of her, and that was that!

But today she had felt almost giddy with exhaustion, she thought wearily, which was why she had been so close to reducing herself to begging a favour of the loathsome Mrs Lodge.

Her thoughts drifted towards how Jamie could possibly have come to employ such a person, and then to his daily commuting to the Sussex boat-yard—how he was coping with it was completely beyond her comprehension.

Just about everything was beyond her comprehension, she realised despondently…her entire ability to reason was being impaired by sheer physical exhaustion brought about by their nights of sexual athletics. Yet it wasn't just that she was physically exhausted, she thought with a pang of fear, reaching out for the black coffee on which she seemed to be existing and gulping down some of it. It was the debilitating mental exhaustion she was finding it so difficult to cope with. To begin with, she had tried time and again to talk to him; each time he had simply walked away, till in the end she had simply given up and stopped trying. They barely spoke, yet their only contact was that most intimate contact of all—and even that puzzled and confused her, even as it thrilled and excited her. At first she had been disturbed and frightened by the power of the needs he had awoken in her, but gradually she had come to recognise her fear as not of her own feelings, but of the oddly manipulative calculation with which he had set about awakening them in her. They were perfectly natural needs and ones which love itself would eventually have ignited in her. But there had been another fear in her initially—that he would lose control and punish her with passion run wild. She gave a small shiver as she remembered, then drained the rest of the fast-cooling coffee. Yet, despite the intensity of his passions, Jamie had never truly lost control…a fact that puzzled and confused her without her being able to fathom out why…though it was also, most confusingly, something she seemed to regard as a plus in his favour, as if it was part of the reason for her loving him more with each passing hour.

She gave a startled jump as the telephone rang and knew she had been on the verge of sleep. She gave Jonathan a quick check and then picked up the receiver.

'Clare—it's great to hear you! How are you—and Graham?'

'Jenny, we're both fine—but what about you?' exclaimed Clare anxiously. 'I've just been speaking to poor Mandy and I feel dreadful!'

'There's no earthly reason for you to feel dreadful,' chided Jenny, amusement in her tone. 'And besides, Mandy told me only today how much better she feels.'

'Jenny, stop being obtuse,' protested Clare. 'Mandy told me all about you having had to take time off from work to look after Jonathan.'

'And it's been wonderful being a full-time aunt—'

'Jenny, you know perfectly well what I mean,' cut in Clare. 'You've only just started that job, so how could you possibly take time off so soon?'

'I'm fortunate to have an understanding boss,' murmured Jenny. Conscious of the bitter irony that had crept into her words, she added hastily. 'So tell me, what sort of progress is being made at your end? There hasn't been much about it in the papers recently.'

'Things are ticking over very well here now—in fact, so well that our unit is pulling out at the weekend—which is one of the reasons I rang.'

Jenny felt a peculiar stillness pervade her, as though everything within her had stalled.

'The reason I rang Mandy first was to ask how she felt about accompanying Jonathan and me to Brussels on Sunday.'

'Did she get the all-clear from her doctor?' asked Jenny. 'She was seeing him this afternoon.'

'She did,' laughed Clare. 'And she was over the moon and raring to go! Though I've warned her I'll be keeping a strict eye on her—believe me, flu is no joke.'

'So, when can we expect you and Graham?' asked Jenny, having to force out the words.

'Unfortunately, Graham's going to have to head straight for Brussels. I'll probably arrive in London some time on Saturday evening—and then out again on Sunday, I'm afraid.'

Though they spoke for several minutes longer, when she finally replaced the receiver, had she tried Jenny would not have been able to call to mind a single thing they had discussed in those minutes.

She leaned back against the cushions as Jamie's words rang harshly in her ears.

'You're out of my life the instant that baby is—and don't you ever forget that.'

No, she hadn't forgotten it, she thought bitterly. How could she ever?

When the telephone started ringing again it was several seconds before she could stir herself sufficiently to answer it.

'Gil,' she stated with a toneless lack of enthusiasm, her mind returning to the present only with considerable difficulty.

'Jenny, I was wondering how you'd feel about a small family house in Chelsea for a few months—rent free,' announced Gil Wardale with a cheerful camaraderie that would no doubt have surprised her had she been feeling a fraction of her usual self. 'It's free now—in fact, you could move in at the weekend if that suited you.'

Suddenly Jenny was acutely alert. 'This weekend?' she asked, her heart beginning to thud uncomfortably.

'Yes.'

'It would most definitely suit me—in fact, your offer couldn't possibly have come at a more opportune time.'

'I'm glad to hear that, Jenny, I really am. And what about your next job?'

'There are some good possibilities in the pipeline,' she lied without compunction, the uncomfortable thud of her heart swiftly abating. His attitude towards her problems leading to her resignation had been callous to say the least, and now his conscience was probably pricking him, she reasoned bitterly.

'Oh dear—I do hope that doesn't rule out your seriously thinking about Australia,' he exclaimed, his patent sincerity startling her.

'Not necessarily,' replied Jenny woodenly, despair filling her at the mere mention of Australia. Why couldn't his wretched brother-in-law have stayed there, she wondered with bitter irrationality, instead of wreaking havoc with her life as he explored the world?

'I'm glad to hear that,' he said quietly, then added, 'Now—about this Chelsea place.' He gave her the address. 'As you can see, it's not terribly far from where you are now, so why don't I just pick you up—say threeish on Sunday afternoon?'

Jenny was frowning as she glanced up from the pad on which she had written the address. 'Gil, there's—'

'How many trips do you reckon it would take to move your things?'

'Gil, there's really no need for you to go to all this trouble on my behalf.'

'Jenny, if you look at it logically, I'm going to very little trouble. We'll have to meet up anyway for me to give you the keys and show you what's what, now, won't we?'

On the verge of flatly refusing the offer, Jenny hesitated, her eyes widening suddenly, almost as though in protest, before a tight, uncharacteristically cynical smile began forming on her lips.

'That's very kind of you, Gil,' she replied brightly. 'One trip will be enough, as I've only a few cases...see you around three on Sunday, then.'

She replaced the receiver with a shaking hand, wondering what demon had possessed her and what on earth such madness was letting her in for.

'Now I know I'm out of my mind!' she groaned aloud, leaping to her feet and going to the pram. 'I think your Auntie Jenny has just arranged for a time bomb to go off on Sunday,' she announced, her eyes suddenly brimming with tears as she gazed down at her beaming nephew. 'Oh, Cuddles, I'm going to miss you more than I ever dreamed possible,' she whispered, reaching down and lifting him into her arms. 'On Sunday we'll both be on our way—you home to Brussels and me...' She broke off, burying her face against his cosy little body, willing the tears not to fall then giving a choked squeal of protest as his tiny hands reached gleefully for her hair and tugged hard.

She took him to the sofa and sat down, her features soft with indulgence as his chubby feet stamped enthusiastically on her lap.

'I honestly don't know what got into me—agreeing to Gil coming round to move me out on Sunday...perhaps I ought to ring him back and suggest I meet him at the new place.'

For several seconds she contemplated the idea, then

angrily shook her head. Why *should* she chicken out? OK, so she couldn't deny she was at fault, having tied herself up in such an inextricable web of lies; but she certainly wasn't the cold-blooded harpie Jamie was so quick to paint her.

'I'm not a bad person, honestly I'm not, Cuddles,' she whispered desperately. 'Yet you name it and your Uncle Jamie's quite happy to believe I'm guilty of it—no matter how despicable.' And there was Gil; cold, uncompromising Gil, who, despite the cosy concern he had just managed to display, had normally little save his business interests at heart. 'I've no compunction about using Gil,' she confided in her happily bouncing nephew, 'because that's no more than he usually does others. I know it's kind of him finding me this place and offering to ferry me around on Sunday, but he certainly wasn't the most understanding of bosses and he managed to make me feel like a pariah over having to take you to his precious offices.' She frowned, her conscience refusing to be appeased even by such unpleasant memories, then exclaimed bitterly, 'And anyway, Gil will merely be an unwitting victim...unlike your Uncle Jamie, who'll be convinced he knows exactly what's going on.'

He had branded her a calculating, husband-stealing bitch, she reminded herself in a sudden rush of almost suffocating anguish, and on Sunday that was exactly what his eyes would see as she brazenly took off with her luggage and her lover.

Though she had told Jamie nothing, it both surprised and disturbed Jenny how quickly he sensed something was afoot. And he had sensed it within moments of arriving home and long before her body had automatically begun undermining her efforts at secrecy with the open des-

peration with which it had tried to blot out all thoughts
of separation by its total abandonment in his.

Although he said nothing, his eyes watched unceas-
ingly, and all day Saturday she lived in fear of Mandy
or Clare—or even Gil—ringing and her having to con-
duct a conversation that would give away nothing under
those relentlessly vigilant eyes.

And when, at nine o'clock that evening, Clare eventually arrived, it was to be greeted by her sister-in-law
with frantic hugs of relief and by her brother with tight-
lipped incomprehension.

'No, I don't want anything to eat, or tea or coffee,'
she protested laughingly as Jenny hovered in clinging
solicitousness around her. 'In fact, all I want is a peek
at my son, a hot bath and then bed.'

Jenny's attempt to accompany Clare to the baby's
room was brought to a jarring halt as Jamie's hands de-
scended like lead weights on to her shoulders.

'Jenny and I were just about to brew some tea,' he
announced. 'Weren't we, Jenny?' he added in a snarl as
Clare disappeared, then propelled Jenny into the kitchen,
closing the door behind them.

'I knew you were up to something,' he informed her
harshly, spinning her around and slamming her up
against the door. 'I suggest you start telling me what it
is.'

'I'd have thought it was perfectly obvious—Clare's
come for Jonathan,' retorted Jenny, refusing to meet his
gaze as she willed herself not to be intimidated.

'And how long ago was this arranged?' he asked, an
icy softness in his voice.

'A few days ago, I think,' she muttered vaguely. 'Oh
dear, did I forget to mention it to you?'

'Oh dear, you did,' he drawled, though she sensed the
control he was now exerting on himself in the sharp

tensing of his body. 'In words, anyway...but I should have known better than to start worrying that you might be deluding yourself about loving me once again—that overwhelming surge of passion I've been treated to for the past couple of nights was simply that sexy little body of yours making hay, so to speak, while the sun still shines, and nothing to do with love.'

'How poetic you are, Jamie,' she managed, inwardly appalled that he had come so close to the truth and then, illogically, even more appalled when she examined his reasons for discarding the truth.

'Where are you going?' he enquired, pulling her against him as she attempted to slip free.

Her body tensed for battle and there was defiance in her eyes as they rose to his.

'I'm going to bed—alone.'

'Alone?' he murmured, as though shocked to the core, then added, in tones of sweet reason, 'It's only when Jonathan's gone that you'll be vacating my bed—or had you forgotten?'

Until that moment she had known that at some point she would contact Gil and put him off—she would simply pick up the telephone and tell him she would make her own way there. Now, as she gazed up into the taunting, cold eyes of the man whose arms still held her, she knew that nothing on this earth would induce her to make that call.

'Let go of me, Jamie,' she ordered calmly. 'Embarrassing though I'd undoubtedly find it, I'm quite prepared to yell loud enough to wake Clare.'

'Clare?' he murmured, chuckling as he released her and placed a patronisingly proprietorial finger under her chin. 'You might be embarrassed, darling, but Clare certainly wouldn't be. She's my sister—remember? She knows all about her brother and his women.'

Without uttering another word, Jenny slipped past him, opened the door and left.

The grief within her was like a volcano about to erupt and against which she fought, terrified of the devastation its escape might wreak in her.

She lay in the dark stillness of her room, the bitterness of her thoughts fuelling the hatred that burned side by side with love in her. That was all she had become— one in the long list of his women. How could he have done this to her? How could she have allowed herself to love a man who could do this to her—could think so low of her?

And as she lay there, hour after lonely hour—hating herself for that terrible loneliness within her that still cried out for him—her only comfort was that demon of pride that had caused so much of the grief she now endured. At least tomorrow, when she walked out of his life, ostensibly on Gil Wardale's arm, any suspicions he might have had about her loving him would be killed stone dead!

Oh yes, her pride would be satisfied, she thought numbly, but at what price? Except that it wasn't such a high price, she answered herself bitterly, burying her face in the pillows, because he had already judged and condemned her.

She lifted her face from the pillow, freezing to stillness as she heard the door open, then immediately close. She lowered her head, scarcely breathing, acutely aware of another presence in the room.

'Jenny?'

She screwed her eyes tightly shut, wanting to scream out in protest against the sudden, joyous leap of her senses. Then she felt the bed react to the weight of another body as he flung himself down on it.

'I don't believe you're asleep,' he informed her in a disgruntled whisper.

For an instant she was tempted to order him out of the bed and the room, but opted for the pretence of sleep.

'And you probably won't believe that I've not come to you racked with lust...but I haven't.'

The bed protested as he heaved himself into a position of more comfort.

'The thing I find most infuriating is that, though I get little enough in the way of sleep when I'm with you, I'm finding it impossible to get a wink of it without you.'

At some point during the night, she half woke and found herself in his arms, and that, their last night together, was their first in which they held one another in an embrace that contained no passion.

When she finally awoke, it was to find herself alone and the first thought that came to her was that the price her pride demanded was too high...and that she must get to a telephone.

Getting to a telephone was one thing, getting hold of Gil Wardale's home number was another she hadn't even thought of. When she discovered he wasn't listed in the telephone directory, her heart sank; on learning from Directory Enquiries that his number was ex-directory, it plummeted to the pit of her stomach.

'You seem a bit...well, jittery,' exclaimed Clare anxiously, entering the living-room to find Jenny guiltily snatching her hand back from the telephone. 'And to be perfectly candid,' she continued, seating herself down next to Jenny and gazing at her with open concern, 'my darling brother appears to be in a similar state. I suppose it's too much to hope you'll be a little less unforthcoming about whatever it is than he is,' she added wryly.

For several terrible seconds Jenny found herself battling against flinging herself into Clare's arms and telling her everything.

'Clare, I just—'

'Mandy's here!' bellowed Jamie from the hall.

Clare hesitated, then gave an apologetic shrug before rising to her feet.

'Jenny, I really think you and I ought to have a chat,' she sighed. 'Perhaps while Jamie's cooking lunch? I must say, I could hardly believe my ears when he offered,' she added as she made her way to the door, her tone slightly bemused.

The instant Clare was gone, Jenny rang Ellie.

'Thank God you're there!' she groaned when Ellie eventually answered.

'You've only just caught me—we were on our way out,' said Ellie. 'Jenny, is something up?'

'Ellie, I'll have to explain another time—but have you Gil's home number?'

'No, I'm afraid I haven't.'

'Oh hell! This is all I need!'

'Jenny what's up? You sound in a right old state!'

'I'm fine,' exclaimed Jenny hastily. 'It's just vital that I speak to Gil right away.' She glanced down at her watch, blanching as she saw how late it was getting.

'What about Laura—his secretary? Hang on and I'll find you her number—she should be able to help.'

Jenny tried the number Ellie had given her immediately, and then almost a dozen times during the space of the next two hours—each time getting no reply. She tried once more, again without success, before they sat down to lunch and accepted her only hope now was if Gil were to arrive late enough for Jamie already to be on his way to the airport with the others.

It was ominously near three by the time she and Clare were clearing up after lunch.

'Mandy, will you do as you're told and stop haring around? You're supposed to be resting,' scolded Clare as Mandy entered the kitchen bearing the remaining dishes from the dining-room.

'You're almost as bad as my mother,' laughed Mandy. 'She keeps ringing me up and nagging me to take it easy. How can I possibly think about anything as mundane as rest when I'm so excited?'

Jenny gave her an affectionate smile, finding it difficult to equate the cool sophistication she had first encountered with the almost schoolgirlish excitement now bubbling in the girl.

'I warn you—Clare's an absolute tartar with patients who don't do as they're told,' she teased.

'But I'm not a patient,' protested Mandy. 'I'm fitter than I've felt for…OK, OK, I'm going,' she laughed, as both Jenny and Clare moved in on her threateningly.

'And, of course, she's perfectly right,' chuckled Clare, then added seriously, 'It's just that I was determined to have a word with you. Jenny, what on earth's up between you and Jamie? You could cut the air between the pair of you with a knife!'

'Clare, I honestly wouldn't know where to begin,' began Jenny agitatedly, then let out a groan of pure terror as the doorbell shrilled loudly. In a state verging on total panic, she grabbed her sister-in-law by the arms. 'Clare, I'll explain everything one day, but for now, please, *please* see if you can keep Jamie out of the way while I answer the door!'

She raced into the hall and dragged open the door.

'Gil—how kind of you,' she managed in a peculiarly croaked whisper.

His pale blue eyes widened in puzzlement.

'Is there something wrong with your voice?' he asked,

his concerned words sounding almost bellowed to Jenny's fear-sensitised ears.

'No—yes, I...Gil, would you mind just waiting there while I get my things?'

'I'll help you—'

'No!' she practically screamed at him, half closing the door in his face before she raced down the hallway to her room.

This was crazy, she chanted to herself, almost in a state of mental collapse. She couldn't possibly just dash out of the place without so much as a word of explanation to Clare...yet she would have to!

Whether to explain to Clare or not became the least of her concerns when she placed the third of her bags outside her bedroom door and saw the lower end of the hall apparently seething with a mass of people.

There were, in fact, only four people by the door—five if she included Jonathan in Mandy's arms. And while Clare looked towards her, raising her hands in a helpless gesture of apology, Jenny balanced two of her cases on top of one another, taking the handle of the lower in her right hand and picked up the third with her left...and started walking.

As she staggered the interminable few yards down the hall towards the front door, she could hear Gil introducing himself—breaking off only when he noticed her approach and made towards her with an offer of assistance.

'Sorry about this,' muttered Jenny with a sickly smile aimed exclusively at her sister-in-law, 'but I didn't get a chance to explain that I'm also moving out today.'

Her head shaking from side to side in complete bemusement, Clare stepped forward and gave her a loving hug.

'Take care,' she whispered, 'and for heaven's sake write to me!'

'I shall,' promised Jenny.

'And what about me?' demanded Jamie icily. 'Don't I get a farewell hug?'

'Jamie, I...' She broke off, stumbling towards the door.

'Well?' he demanded harshly.

Desperate to escape, she uttered the first words that entered her head.

'Thank you, Jamie...thank you for having me.'

'Having you, Jennifer?' he queried venomously. 'It was a pleasure.'

CHAPTER TEN

THE one thought that unaccountably kept churning through Jenny's head was that she hadn't kissed Jonathan goodbye.

Had she been in a fit state she would have been most grateful for Gil Wardale's silence as he drove her to her new home, and also more than a little discomfited by the several puzzled glances he threw in her direction.

It was a small town house, she noticed with scant interest as they arrived, a house pretty much like a million others, except that this one's location made it worth a small fortune.

Still maintaining a slightly wary silence, Gil let her into the house, returning a few moments later with her luggage.

'You're obviously in no mood to be shown around,' he stated quietly. 'So how about if I make us some tea? The kitchen's down there and John's left in a few supplies.'

He tapped her lightly on the arm when she showed no signs of having heard him.

'Jenny?'

'I—oh sorry...I was miles away,' she stammered.

'Come along—I'll get that tea on,' he said, firmly taking her by the arm and leading her to the kitchen.

It was as they stepped into clinical brightness of the kitchen that Jenny was suddenly hit by an overwhelming awareness of what had happened...and then it was as though her entire being was being assaulted by every negative emotion conceivable.

'Gil, I…I'm sorry,' she blurted out, trying desperately to retain control of herself for just a few moments longer. 'You've been most kind, but I'm just about to make the most colossal fool of myself and I'd rather do it alone.'

'That's the trouble—kindness was something noticeably lacking in my treatment of you,' he stated woodenly. 'I…you…' He broke off with an exclamation of vexation. 'Why be coy about it?' he demanded, as though remonstrating with himself. 'My conscience has been troubling me over you!'

'Why? You had no option but to accept my resignation,' protested Jenny, the sheer unexpectedness of his words shocking her out of her state of imminent disintegration.

'I realise that,' he retorted, 'but—'

'And there's absolutely no reason for you to feel the slightest guilt over me,' cut in Jenny, determined to put an end to this once and for all—the last thing she needed was to be subjected to listening to this man wallowing in remorse! 'You see, this afternoon I used you in the most despicable fashion.'

'I suppose you're referring to your using my presence to arouse the Castile guy's jealousy,' he murmured mildly, strolling to the sink and filling the kettle while Jenny's gaze followed him in wide-eyed astonishment.

'You're not furious?' she croaked.

'Why should I be furious?' he enquired, plainly amused. 'I have to admit, though, to some surprise at how unqualified a success your ploy was…the poor man was almost beside himself with fury, despite the coolness with which he managed to handle it.'

'I can't believe I'm hearing this,' protested Jenny dazedly, drawing out a chair at the scrubbed wood kitchen table and sinking weakly on to it. 'I've thought

I've been losing my reason once or twice during the past few days—now I'm certain I have!' she added glumly.

'I know most people think I'm a pretty heartless character,' he muttered ruefully. 'But you're the first to tell me that discovering I have the rudiments of understanding in me makes them question their sanity.'

He flashed her the ghost of a self-mocking smile before reaching down mugs from one of the cupboards and busying himself with preparing the tea. Unable to find any words, Jenny watched him in bemused fascination, finding it impossible to equate these relaxed, almost domesticated actions with the robotic Gil Wardale for whom she had so briefly worked.

He brought a tray to the table and sat down.

'I'd forgotten what a big, comfortable kitchen this was,' he said, glancing around him. 'It was Sally, my wife, who suggested offering you the use of this place before we move in.'

'This is *your* house?' exclaimed Jenny, now completely confused.

He nodded.

'So why aren't you moving in immediately?' she demanded, her tone suspicious.

'A friend is buying our flat—but not for another few months. And anyway, we bought this place three years ago—soon after Sally became pregnant.'

Jenny took over the pouring of the tea as he had shown no signs of doing so.

'She miscarried a month later,' he continued, 'and we've rented the place out ever since.'

'Oh, Gil, I am sorry,' gasped Jenny.

'We were both devastated…but, as you've probably gathered, I'm not a man who lets his emotions show easily—though I was hiding them, I thought, for Sally's sake. I had my work to bury myself in, and I took to doing so totally when a car accident brought on Sally's second miscarriage a year later.'

'Your poor wife,' whispered Jenny, her eyes blurring over.

He took one of the mugs she had poured but forgotten about completely, giving her a strained, slightly embarrassed smile as he did so.

'I didn't mean to ramble on,' he apologised. 'It's just that, when I told Sally about your resignation, she came right out with it and asked me if I was feeling guilty about it because a baby had been involved…and from there we began talking; I mean really speaking to one another as we hadn't for almost two years. You see, I'd honestly believed that by not mentioning the subject of babies I was making things easier for her.'

'And I suppose she felt as though she'd let you down by not having the child you wanted,' sighed Jenny.

He gave her a slightly startled look. 'That's exactly how she felt, and it shattered me to hear her say so! I've now managed to convince her of the truth…that she and her happiness are all I've ever wanted for my life to be complete.'

'And I'm sure that was just what she'd been longing to hear,' croaked Jenny, her words hampered by a large lump in her throat.

'It was then that the real Sally re-emerged,' he exclaimed with unselfconscious delight. 'Even though she was already then sickening for a bad dose of flu. In fact, she was all for coming along with me today, but the weather was so awful that I persuaded her to stay tucked up in front of the fire—but she'd like to meet you. Will you come and have dinner with us when she's a hundred per cent over this wretched flu?'

'I'd love to,' smiled Jenny, still too lost in his totally

unexpected disclosures to appreciate the merciful distraction they had provided her from her own problems.

'And I'm sure she'll do her best to sell you the Australian job—that's where she's from,' he grinned, glancing down at his watch, then rising to his feet. 'Now—perhaps I should show you around before I go.'

Jenny rose too, shaking her head, her own problems now beginning to loom back into focus. 'No—you get off home; I'll enjoy exploring on my own.'

He turned to her as they reached the front door, his expression a mixture of anxiety and uncertainty.

'Jenny, forgive me if this seems grossly out of turn...but one thing Sally and I have learned the hard way is that love deserves the truth, no matter how much circumstances may appear to indicate the contrary.'

Jenny nodded—where a two-way love was concerned, there was no question that he was right.

'Perhaps you and Castile should take a leaf out of our book...because honest is not what you were being with him today. I'm sorry,' he muttered, unmistakably embarrassed when she made no reply. 'I really had no right whatever to interfere.'

'No—you spoke as any friend would,' she stated quietly. 'And only a fool would disagree with you.'

'I'm glad you accept it was said only in friendship.' He handed her the door keys. 'I'll get Sally to give you a ring about coming round.'

As the door closed behind him, Jenny gazed around herself, her eyes skimming sightlessly from the mottled russet of the floor tiles to her three pieces of luggage standing at the foot of the staircase. Then her body slid slowly to the floor and the grief within her, now too vast to contain, overflowed and engulfed her.

That night and for the two that followed it, what little sleep she had was broken by a dream. It was the same dream each time, yet it was hardly even a dream; more a remembering of that last night with Jamie. In reality she had woken to find herself in his arms; in the dream the sequence became reversed: it was when she discovered herself to be in his arms that she would awaken.

For the better part of those nights she lay awake, at times cursing him, at times tormenting herself with the conundrum of why, on that last night, he had felt compelled to seek her out—the woman he despised—in order to achieve the sleep he craved.

It was on the third day, when she realised the basic provisions she had been left had virtually run out, that she made a concerted attempt to start pulling herself together.

She sternly reminded herself that, even if she decided to take up Gil's offer in Australia, there could be no mooning around the place doing nothing for the next few months. For a start, she needed to do something to replenish her fast-dwindling funds. Having decided that she should start looking for some temporary work as a matter of urgency, she spent the morning unpacking and ironing the more crumpled of her clothes.

At midday she toyed with the idea of ringing a few agencies and realised then that she seemed almost to be putting off the moment when she would step out of the house…for the first time in three days, she reminded herself edgily, disturbed by the completely alien nature of her behaviour.

'No—you'll go out and visit those agencies in person—and do it this afternoon,' she told herself firmly, then had to shrug off the pang of alarm at the realisation that she had just started talking to herself.

A sense of unease spurring her determination, she selected what she would wear, laid it out on the bed and then went to have a bath.

She had only just stepped out of the bath when she heard the doorbell. Flinging on a towelling robe, she raced down the stairs to the door.

'Gil!' she exclaimed, opening the door wider. 'Do excuse me, I've just had a rather late bath.'

'Sorry about that. I'd better not keep you chatting on the doorstep,' he apologised, stepping inside. 'I tried ringing you this morning and discovered there's been a misunderstanding over the telephone—I'm afraid you're disconnected at the moment. I've been on to them and they've promised to get it sorted out.'

'I hadn't noticed,' said Jenny, 'but thanks for doing something about it. Would you like a cup of tea—or coffee, perhaps?' Preferably without milk, she thought with a pang, remembering the shopping she had to do.

He shook his head, smiling—a trifle sheepishly, Jenny thought, then decided it must be the light.

'No, I wouldn't, thanks—I'm on my way home for lunch.'

Now certain it had been a sheepish smile after all, Jenny smiled back—she was growing rather fond of this new Gil Wardale.

'I just popped round to tell you about the telephone— oh, and to give you these.' He reached in his coat pocket and handed her a spare set of house keys. 'And also to remind you that Sally will be ringing you—once you have a telephone.'

'And I'll be looking forward to hearing from her,' replied Jenny, touched by the sudden glow that seemed to illuminate him the moment he mentioned his wife's name, and also a little puzzled by the fact that he seemed to be dithering about going. 'Shouldn't you be getting a move on if she's expecting you for lunch?' she added gently, and found herself having to adjust mentally to the fact that she felt sufficiently at ease with him to make such a remark.

He turned slightly as she smiled and pointedly opened the door.

'Yes, I...we're going to have a baby,' he blurted out, plainly no longer able to contain himself. 'In fact, Sally's almost five months pregnant!'

'Oh, Gil, that's wonderful!' she exclaimed delightfully. 'But almost five months—and you hadn't even noticed?'

'I thought she'd put on a bit of weight,' he admitted sheepishly. 'She was going to tell me the night I told you about...the doctor had told her there was absolutely no reason to fear anything would go wrong. But that day she'd started feeling so rough with the flu she was about to get that she got scared and decided to put off telling me for a while.'

'She must have been worried out of her mind, poor thing!' exclaimed Jenny.

'Our doctor's now given her yet another thorough check—and a strong talking-to—and has told her she's carrying a normal, healthy baby and will do so to full term.'

'Oh, Gil, what fantastically wonderfully news!' she exclaimed delightedly, his bashful joy so infecting her that she reached up and gave him an exuberant peck on the cheek.

For an instant his eyes widened in surprise, then his face resumed its expression of bemused delight and he turned and left.

Jenny closed the door behind him, that infectious delight still lingering on her own face. Not long ago she would have described him as a cold-hearted workaholic, and now she knew him to be a warm, rather shy man capable of walking on air because he and the wife he so loved would soon become parents. Then suddenly the delight began dying on her face and a picture of Jonathan crept into her mind. With it came the aching realisation that any baby she and Jamie might have had would have stood a good chance of looking very like Jonathan.

Angry that such a ridiculous thought should even have entered her head, she made her way down the hallway, her face now tense with bitterness. She halted at the foot of the stairs, inwardly groaning as the doorbell rang again.

Wondering what Gil had forgotten in his bemused state of delirium, she returned to the door, vowing to put all thought of Jonathan and his genetic make-up firmly from her mind.

She opened the door. 'You're going to be late…' She slammed it shut in an action that was purely reflex.

'Jenny, open this bloody door!' roared Jamie, attacking both it and the doorbell simultaneously. 'I'll get the jack out of my car and jemmy it open if you don't!' he threatened at the top of his lungs, while at the same time releasing the bell to hammer on the door with both his fists.

Convinced the door would collapse any moment if she didn't, she opened it and raced to the stairs.

'You don't have to run away—I'm not going to attack you,' he yelled after her, slamming the door shut behind him. 'In fact, I doubt if I could,' he muttered, gazing down at his right hand and flexing it gingerly. 'I've probably broken the damned thing.'

'Serves you right!' Jenny howled at him, having to fight off an appalling urge to race to him and fling herself into his arms. 'How dare you—?'

'Why the hell do you always have to prefix anything

you say to me with the words "how dare you"?' he demanded, flinging up both his arms in disgust.

'What do you want? Why are you here? Who gave you this address?' babbled Jenny, terrified she was about to lose the battle she was waging with herself, and with it her mind. 'And what—?'

'Hold on, will you?' he protested angrily, ramming his hands into his pockets and leaning back against the door as he glowered across the hallway at her. 'There are only so many questions I can cope with at one time! I'll start with that last one first—*you* told me the address.'

'Very funny,' she retorted scathingly.

'What's wrong, Jenny—did I use it too soon for your liking?' he drawled. 'I must say, it could have made things a little awkward for you had I walked slap into lover-boy on his way out—which I almost did.'

'For God's sake, stop being so ridiculous,' she snapped. 'And anyway, you know perfectly well I didn't give you this address.'

'You left it on the telephone pad—which is as near as damn it to giving me it as I can think of. I really can't think how I didn't notice it until today.'

'You...I...you can't possibly believe this drivel you're talking! Keep away from me!' she shrieked as he began striding angrily towards her.

'Why—because you know you can't trust yourself with me?' he taunted, halting a few paces from her. 'Because you know all I have to do is touch you and you're mine for the taking?'

'Jamie, please,' she begged, convinced now that she would lose her reason if she didn't unburden herself, once and for all, of those lies with which she had so damned herself. 'Please, Jamie, you've got to—'

'To answer your questions,' he cut in with deliberate

obtuseness. 'The second one, if I remember rightly, was why am I here—and the first, what do I want? I think we might as well lump those together as one, don't you?'

'Jamie, please! Stop it—I don't want to hear!' The words seemed to explode from her. 'I've told you nothing but a pack of lies! I've no relationship whatever with Gil Wardale and I never have had—apart from his being my boss for a brief period. You've got to believe me! He's a happily married man...his wife's going to have a baby, for heaven's sake!'

'So, what's this happily married man—one about to become a father, no less—doing keeping you in this place?'

'He *isn't* keeping me here. I—'

'Don't tell me,' he snarled. 'Let me guess. You're renting it for yourself! How many other unemployed women do you know able to afford a Chelsea town house?'

'I'm *caretaking* it for Gil and his wife till they sell their flat!' she shrieked, scrabbling frantically up a further couple of stairs as he suddenly moved forward and flung himself down on the bottom one.

'At least credit me with some intelligence,' he flung at her contemptuously. 'That nauseating little scene I just witnessed on the doorstep tells a very different tale. Hell, I thought the man was supposed to be a workaholic!' he raged, scorn burning in his eyes as they rose to hers. 'Yet it would appear he works part-time now he's in your delicate clutches.'

'He came round here on his way home for lunch,' stated Jenny, a terrible lethargy creeping over her as she wondered why she was wasting her breath. Fighting that lethargy, she forced herself to continue, her words stammered and halting. 'He came to tell me the telephone's been accidentally disconnected...and to remind me I'm having dinner with him and his wife one night this week.'

'One thing I'll give you, Jenny—you're almost convincing,' he exclaimed bitterly. 'Or, at least, you would be if I were a half-wit—which I'm not...not all of the time, anyway.'

'Jamie, I'm telling you the truth,' she pleaded hoarsely. 'I've told you so many lies that I've lost track of them...but I'm telling you the truth now, though I realise I can hardly expect you to believe that.'

'No—you can't!' he exclaimed with savage venom. 'Because no woman in her right mind would tell anyone the sort of lies you claim to have told me. Lies that brand her as nothing more than a cheap, conniving, marriage-wrecking little tart!'

'Is that how you see me?' she asked hoarsely, finding herself unable to face up to actually hearing him speak those words.

'Damn it, Jenny, do you think I find it easy to think that—of you of all people?' he rasped. 'But what the hell else can I think?'

'You can think of no reason why I should tell you— of all people—such lies?' she asked, trembling as though on the brink of something irrevocable.

He turned away from her, his shoulders hunching as he clenched his arms across his knees.

'No—I can think of no reason why any sane woman would tell such lies.'

'What about an insane woman?' she asked, knowing now that the time had come for her self-destructive pride to pay the price of its wrongs in full. 'I doubt if I could have been described as completely sane at sixteen, when I first fell in love with you. And certainly not at nineteen—I mean, any sane person would have taken the hint so subtly given…when you laughed at me, then threw me out of your bed in disgust.'

'Jenny, any disgust was purely in your imagination,' he protested.

'But, unfortunately, I wasn't sure,' she continued relentlessly, the words queueing up in her mind and demanding their say no matter what. 'Though things did change a little once I arrived at the age of twenty-three and found my affliction still securely intact…because then I actually acknowledged the fact that I wasn't sane.'

'Jenny, for God's sake—'

'And I realised that all I could do was cling to the hope that one day I would be cured…I didn't care how, just so long as I could believe that day would at some time come.'

'Why?' he groaned out in pained exasperation.

'Would *you* like to spend the rest of your life insane?' she demanded sharply, angered by his reaction.

'Jenny, why do you equate loving me with insanity, for God's sake?'

'Would *you* like to be in love with you?' she flung at him accusingly. 'If you were a woman, that is?'

'This is crazy!' he exploded, swinging round to face her, his expression frozen in disbelief. 'Jenny, why the hell couldn't you just come out with it and admit how you felt?'

'Why? Because I have my pride!' she raged and knew, the instant the words were out, how ludicrous they were—a fact confirmed by the incredulous groan with which he greeted them.

'You'd rather I believed you were some sort of home-wrecking whore than know you loved me?'

'Yes…no! All I did was pluck Gil's name out of the air,' she protested. 'I'd no idea he was married—I'm not *that* stupid,' she added indignantly.

'Jenny, could you just try explaining to me why loving me is such a terrible thing?' he asked quietly.

'What's the point in loving someone who'll never love you?' she asked with a defeated shrug.

She had said all she had to say, she thought dejectedly, and where had it got her? Now all she wanted to do was curl up in a ball and sleep—preferably forever.

'First let's deal with those other questions you asked,' he suggested in a curiously flat tone.

The shrug she gave this time was one of complete indifference; the feeling of exhausted detachment now seeping through her left her too drained even to feel surprise that he should revert to a subject that could no longer have any possible relevance.

'Jenny, I came here today, believing that this was where you were living with another man. Despite that belief, I came here to ask you to leave…come home to me.'

The fact that he had said 'come home to' when he should have said 'with' entered her mind and hovered there before she cast it wearily aside.

'Well?' he demanded.

'Well what?' she groaned, wishing he would have the decency to go and leave her in some semblance of peace. 'Jamie, I realise you didn't approve of me living with a married man, but I've just explained, for heaven's sake—I wasn't!'

'I wanted you anyway,' he muttered.

'You what?' she demanded, the lethargy miraculously deserting her. 'What you mean is that you discovered lust isn't as easily switched off as you'd thought!' she accused, hating him.

'It's probably a darn sight easier to switch off than love,' he retorted angrily, grabbing her by the ankles and hauling her down the stairs towards him.

'I hate you!' she screamed, pummelling against his chest with her fists as he pulled her against him. 'I might have known you'd stoop low enough to fling that back in my face, because you never missed an opportunity to remind me of the fool I made of myself when I was nineteen! You're despicable! I hate you!'

'So, it worked, did it?' he demanded, imprisoning her flailing fists against his chest as he dragged her fully into his arms. 'You told me all those lies, and miraculously you stopped loving me after all those terrible years?'

As his lips found hers, a shudder so violent rippled through him that it distracted her long enough for her body to dispossess her mind. And her arms reached out to cling around him as her lips answered his in a frenzy of welcome.

'I hate you,' she sobbed, her arms straining fiercely around him.

'Jenny, I hope to God you've just resorted to lying again,' he whispered huskily. 'I couldn't take you recovering your sanity now that I've lost mine for all time.'

'And you have the nerve to ask me why I didn't confide the truth in you!' she shrieked, pushing him violently from her and toppling him off the stairs in the process. 'I'll tell you why,' she raged on, leaping to her feet. 'Because I knew you'd ridicule me—and I was right!'

'Jenny, this is crazy!' he exclaimed angrily, grabbing hold of her by an ankle as she made the error of trying to step over his prone body. 'Is there *nothing* I can say that you're not going to take offence over? For God's sake, Jenny, I'm trying to tell you—'

'Let go of my foot,' she cut in frigidly, trying desperately to hang on to a shred of dignity while at the same time having to cling to the banister to prevent herself from toppling over.

'No.'

'Jamie, for heaven's sake stop being so…so ridiculous!'

'Ridiculous?' he echoed in outrage. 'Here I am, prostrated at your feet—and all you do is complain about how ridiculous I look!'

'I didn't say you *looked* ridiculous,' she argued wearily, wondering why she had bothered wasting her breath while tugging half-heartedly to free herself. 'Jamie, I—'

'Well, I can tell you, I feel bloody ridiculous,' he growled. 'And do you know what I'm wishing right at this very minute?' he demanded morosely.

'No—but I'm sure you'll regale me with every last detail of it,' she snapped.

'Too right I shall—I'm wishing I followed my instincts of several years ago—four, to be precise—and emigrated to the other side of the world from you.'

'Really?' she enquired scathingly, tempted to tell him that was precisely how she intended escaping him, but opting instead for praying he would lose interest in this sadistic baiting of her, and simply pick himself up and go home.

'To be honest—no,' he sighed, in tones that brought every nerve in her body to suspicious alertness. 'That's not what I wish. Hell, Jenny, I always suspected it would be bad if it ever actually happened—but even a pessimist such as I am couldn't have envisaged it would be this ghastly…and the ridiculous thing is that it's ghastly for all the wrong reasons.'

'Jamie, would you mind telling me what you're waffling on about?' she demanded sharply, and was immediately berating herself for having come out with so guileless a question.

'I'm not waffling. Damn it, Jenny, I'm talking about love!'

'And I suppose this is merely another manifestation of your perverted sense of humour,' she rounded on him angrily, humiliatingly aware of the ludicrous spectacle she must be presenting—her foot trapped in mid-air and her arms wrapped round the banister in her struggle to remain upright.

'So now you've added a perverted sense of humour to that endless tally you keep of all my faults!' he exclaimed in outrage. 'And what I'd like to know is what you base all these judgements of yours on. Take my alleged irresponsibility, for example—I'd have thought my behaviour on the night of Clare's and Graham's wedding—'

'That's right—fling that in my face again!' she raged, unable to believe that he had actually reverted to dredging it up yet again.

'OK, I admit there was selfishness in my actions as well,' he hurled back at her, sitting upright while still maintaining his hold on her foot—an action that left her clinging to the banister as though for her life. 'But I damned well *wasn't* irresponsible, even if my reasoning was crazy!'

'Jamie, let go of my foot!'

'No—not till you've heard me out! Jenny, I knew there was only one woman I was ever in danger of falling in love with—'

'Yes—danger!' she cut in scathingly. 'You want to try examining your pathetic aversion to love,' she continued, pain and anger now pouring from her in an unstoppable flow of bitterness. 'Why bother to live if

you're so terrified of life's pain that you can't afford to
risk what's supposed to be one of its greatest joys?'

'Jenny, if you'd just shut up for a moment—'

'Why—because you can't take the truth?'

'No, because...for heaven's sake, this is ridiculous!'
he exploded, suddenly releasing her foot and leaping to
his feet. 'Why the hell do you always have to make
things fifty times more complicated than they already
are?' he demanded, his eyes locked in hostile confron-
tation with hers.

For an instant he appeared to be about to take a step
towards her, then he spun round and marched towards
the door.

'Jamie...what are you doing?' she croaked, leaping to
her feet and stumbling down the stairs, unable to accept
that he was actually contemplating leaving even though,
seconds before, that was what she had prayed for.

'I'm trying to collect my wits!' he exclaimed, halting
suddenly, his back still to her.

Jenny halted too, shocked to discover she had been
racing after him.

'OK—let's try a different tack,' he growled, spinning
around and striding back to her, 'starting with, I love
you,' he finished, reaching out and pulling her into his
arms.

She made no attempt to resist, conscious only of a
leaden limpness in herself as the silence between them
began to lengthen ominously.

'Well—that raised a bundle of laughs, didn't it?' he
observed flatly, drawing back slightly from her to gaze
down into her pale, almost frightened face. 'Oh, Jenny—
forgive me,' he whispered contritely, hugging her
fiercely to him. 'Can't you see I'm so terrified out of my
wits that I'm...I'm attempting to do a Jenny on you?'

'You're not making any sense,' she protested weakly,

her mind still grappling with his earlier words and frantically trying to decode what there was no way she could allow herself to accept at face value.

'As a kid you were famed for your calamitous attempts at clowning your way out of tight corners…and I'm beginning to realise you resorted to it again with me not so long ago. Jenny, my darling, I've been aware for quite a few years now that you're the one woman I'd love if ever I allowed you to get near enough to me. I've fought it for so long that now I'm having a real problem stringing the right words together…but clowning obviously isn't the way to do it.'

'You make it sound so…so horrible,' she whispered dazedly, forced to take his words at face value yet numbingly aware of their negative lack of joy.

'Jenny, I think it's about time we started being honest with one another—horrible is one word that accurately describes much of what we've put ourselves through… though I could come up with a few far stronger ones.' He dropped his head to hers, pressing his cheek against her temple as she shivered in his arms. 'Jenny, the nightmare of it all for me is that, as I discovered that my pathetic aversion to love, as you so rightly describe it, was based on no more than childhood misconceptions and hang-ups that bore no relationship to adult reality— you were driving me insane with your crazy litany of lies!'

'Jamie, are you saying that if I hadn't told you all those lies…you wouldn't have minded loving me?' she asked shakily, feeling decidedly alarmed by the problem she was having assembling her thoughts, let alone putting them into words.

'Minded?' he groaned, half laughing. 'What sort of a word is that? Jenny, I'd have been ecstatic about loving you…I *am* ecstatic about loving you!'

'I…you…Jamie, you really can't expect me to believe you,' she croaked, her problems now being added to by the unformed feelings rearing up in her and taking violent exception to those stammered, negative words.

With a soft groan of exasperation, he turned her in his arms and marched her to the stairs, then sat her down on them and joined her.

'Wouldn't you like to sit somewhere more comfortable?' she asked dazedly. 'There's the—'

'No—the less I see of this place, the easier I feel,' he muttered, slipping an arm around her and drawing her firmly against him. 'Jenny, nothing I say can change the way I've behaved and the harm I've done…and there's no point my denying that I was so frightened of what love seemed to entail that I was quite prepared, as you said, to renounce one of life's greatest joys. I saw love only in terms of the devastation it caused my mother when my father died…and, no matter how much she managed to pull herself together eventually, she never returned to being the person she was before his death.'

'Surely that's the only way it can be if you love someone above all else,' muttered Jenny, a feeling akin to guilt entering the joyless voice within her at the acknowledgement that she could never be the same were something to happen to him.

She loved him, she thought miserably, and he had just told her he loved her—he *had*!—and the only positive feeling she was experiencing at this very minute was guilt that she could empathise with his mother's loss!

'Jenny, can't you see that's what I could never grasp?' he pleaded, his arm tightening around her as she angrily tried to break free. 'And which is why I felt I had no option but to run from you when you were only nineteen. Jenny, I was only too aware of how you felt about me then. The evening of the wedding, when we were danc-

ing and you were looking up at me from those big, blue,
love-filled eyes of yours...hell, it's crazy, but my mind
began cooking up just about every gory end I could possibly meet...and your face began changing before my
eyes, becoming indistinguishable from that of my
mother all those years before.'

'And do you honestly think that by walking out of my
life you could prevent what I actually would have felt
had any of your gory imaginings come true?' she demanded bitterly.

'Jenny, I was thinking about no one but myself,' he
sighed. 'That's what I'm trying to explain to you—how
mixed up my reasoning was, and how unspeakably selfish my actions were...and I'm also trying to explain to
you that I can see myself for what I was; that nobility
had nothing to do with my resisting you and that all I
have to show for my self-centred preoccupation with my
own hang-ups is at least four wasted years...years that
could have been spent loving you.'

He cupped her chin in his hand, forcing her to meet
his gaze. And as she looked into his face she felt life
stir within her and feeling begin to return to her numbed
mind and body. And then she closed her eyes, unable to
take any more as love and the inescapable knowledge of
being loved threatened to fill her to overflowing.

'I suppose it's pointless cursing my lousy timing,' he
muttered, the hopelessness in his words forcing Jenny's
eyes open and her mind to attempt concentrating itself
on things other than the bliss intoxicating it. 'I was still
in my teens when Clare had a go at straightening me
out—accusing me of mentally erasing all the years of
happiness our parents had shared and of thinking only
in terms of the pain of Dad's death...as though all the
good and beautiful things no longer counted. I can see
now, it was impossible for me to understand what she

meant until I had accepted loving you.' For several seconds he gazed down at her, his thumb rubbing restlessly against the curve of her jaw. 'But even though I'd accepted it, I still managed to blow it. Yet, no matter what you may think, it was love with which my body was bombarding yours in those last nights we spent together…then, on that very last night, I was trying to tell you I had a need for you far greater than sex. As I say—I managed to blow it, and in every way imaginable.' As he uttered those last words he released her chin and removed his arm from around her. 'Well—I suppose that just about covers what I wanted to say,' he muttered with uncharacteristic awkwardness, then got to his feet. 'You don't have to see me to the door,' he announced as he began walking away from her.

Only too aware that her mind was not functioning in the least normally and that there was probably something she should be doing, Jenny none the less watched him walk away in stunned stupefaction.

'I had no intention of seeing you to the door,' she called out after him, then shook her head in bewilderment—why on earth had she come out with that?

He halted, but didn't turn.

'And I didn't ask you to,' he snapped.

Jenny frowned, her eyes on his tall, motionless figure as she took comforting stock of the happiness still lurking so secretively within her…he loved her, so what was all this about?

'I thought you were supposed to have got your mind straightened out as to what love's all about,' she stated eventually—and decided that even that was all wrong.

'I have, but I've still managed to botch it all up.'

'You haven't.'

'Haven't what?'

'Got any idea what love's about if you think I'm about to let you slink off like that.'

'I'm not slinking off!' he exclaimed morosely. 'I may not be the most sensitive of men, but even I can tell when I've blown any chance I might have had.'

Jenny counted slowly up to ten, all the while reminding herself that he loved her, after which she inspected her fingernails for a further five seconds; then she gave a soft groan and buried her face in her lap, convulsed with laughter.

'Jenny? Darling, please don't cry!' he begged, racing back to her and dragging her to her feet and into his arms.

'Jamie, could you just try explaining to me why you were going?' she demanded, laughter still racking her.

'Because you wanted me to. Jenny…my God, you're laughing!'

'What on earth else can I do?' she groaned exasperatedly. 'Jamie Castile, I've loved you since I was twelve and I'll no doubt love you for the rest of my life.'

'You will?' he queried suspiciously.

'And you waltz in here,' she continued, ignoring his interruption, 'and tell me you love me and start waltzing back out, muttering vague utterances about my wanting you to!'

'That's the impression I got,' he protested. 'Jenny, the more I tried to explain how I feel about you, the less enthusiasm you seemed to show with each word I uttered.'

'What did you expect—somersaults? Jamie, I—'

'Yes—a few somersaults would have done nicely.'

'Jamie Castile, you egotistical…' Her indignant words deteriorated into groaned laughter. 'Funnily enough, now that you mention it—that's exactly what I feel like doing!'

'Sorry, but it's too late,' he muttered uncooperatively. 'But you could try putting your arms around me and kissing me instead.'

She did precisely that, wondering what had prevented her from doing it the instant it had sunk in that he actually did love her—followed by at least a dozen or so somersaults.

'Oh, Jenny, don't ever punish me like this again,' he begged with a shudder, his arms tightening suffocatingly around her as his lips began frantic exploration of hers.

'Jamie, what on earth do you mean—punish you?' she protested breathlessly as his exploring mouth moved to search against her cheek.

'You didn't seem like you any more...it was as though my loving you was the last thing you wanted,' he whispered huskily. 'You've already admitted that loving me is something you can't wait to be cured of...I thought my terrible behaviour had shown you it wouldn't be too difficult.'

'Jamie, I love you,' she protested softly, thrown by the unmistakable desperation in his words. 'It's a love that's completely incurable—no matter how I may have tried to kid myself. And as for your terrible behaviour...I was directly responsible for causing it with all those ghastly lies I kept telling you. Jamie, it was all my fault.'

'Come to think of it—they were absolutely diabolical lies,' he sighed, laughter softening the tension from his features as he drew back and gazed down at her.

'They were,' she agreed indignantly. 'They even prevented me from letting fly at you over losing my job...but it was all my fault anyway that you didn't ring me,' she added sadly.

'Darling, nothing gave me the right to put you through all that,' he whispered, then grinned down evilly at her when she shook her head in protest. 'Mind you, I was punished a hundredfold—how I kept my hands from your throat when you claimed to have made love to me simply in order to—'

'Stop it!' she begged, pressing her lips fiercely against his in an effort to silence him.

'And then, when you said—'

'Jamie, please!'

'It's going to take me years to recover from it. And years of devoted loving on your part for me to be able to consider forgiving you—I hope you realise that.'

'I do, I do…Jamie, I love you!'

'That's all very well,' he murmured with malevolent contentment. 'But I'll have to insist this undertaking of yours is all legal and above board—there's no way I'm allowing you to renege on it.'

'We can visit a solicitor first thing in the morning if that will make you happy,' she chuckled, the sound of her own laughter suddenly bringing her acute awareness of the magnitude of the happiness bubbling within her.

'A solicitor?' he demanded in feigned bemusement. 'Since when have solicitors conducted marriage cere-monies?'

Jenny felt the breath catch painfully in her throat—only an instant ago she was wallowing in the magnitude of her happiness—and now it had become too much for her to manage and was threatening to suffocate her.

'Perhaps I shouldn't have asked you cold like that!' he exclaimed anxiously. 'Jenny, it goes without saying I'll give up open sea racing if that's what you want.'

'Jamie, you're mad!'

'I'll give up racing all together—'

'That's not what I meant!' she almost squeaked in her exasperation. 'The man I love races yachts—and hap-pens to do so brilliantly. He also promised to give me some lessons…but if he intends reneging on that promise—'

'Jenny, your face was a picture of terror when you watched that race on the television,' he protested huskily. 'And I think it was seeing your face that brought it home to me how irrevocably I loved you…because I knew that, if you'd turned to me and asked me to give up racing, I'd have agreed to—and meant it—without a qualm.'

'And yet all you did was make snide remarks about how lucky I was that Gil was in a safe job,' she groaned.

'I wish you wouldn't mention his name so casually,' he muttered.

'Jamie, it was Gil who suggested the other day that you and I should indulge in some of the honesty he and Sally, his wife, have,' she chided gently. 'He pointed out that love deserves the truth…something you and I have found out the hard way.'

'The hardest way possible,' he agreed hoarsely. 'But my wounds are still a little too raw to cope with hearing his name without wincing—and besides, I'm having decided problems over the fact that you haven't yet answered the question I asked you.'

'The answer is no,' she replied without hesitation.

'I knew this was all too good to be true,' he groaned.

'Jamie, you *are* mad!' exclaimed Jenny. 'You'd be like a zombie if you didn't race, and besides, I can't wait to learn!'

'Jenny, forget the damned boats—the question I asked you was, will you marry me?'

'Only as long as there's no more talk about you giving up— '

'Jenny, will you or won't you marry me?'

She nodded, then buried her face against him, trying to get enough air into her lungs to support speech.

'Of course I will,' she choked. 'I love you...of course I'll marry you.'

'Thank God we've managed to get that sorted out,' he groaned with relief. 'Now—do you mind if we get your things and go home?'

She blinked up at him in bewilderment. 'Right this minute?'

'Right this very instant,' he stated firmly, then pulled a small, slightly embarrassed face. 'Perfectly nice though this house is—it gives me the creeps. Darling, all those things I came here believing...I still can't seem to shake my mind completely free of them.'

'I'll get my things this very instant!' she exclaimed breathlessly, making to turn and finding herself trapped. 'But you'll have to let go of me.'

'I'm not sure if I can,' he murmured with a lazy grin that started her heart somersaulting. 'Did I tell you how much I love you?'

She shook her head, a surfeit of happiness rendering speech impossible.

'I thought not,' he chuckled. 'Well, the truth is, I love you so much...so much.' He lowered his head to hers, his breath soft against her lips. 'So very much...Jenny, I think we'd better get you packed and us out of here...I'll feel a lot less tongue-tied at home.'

'You...tongue-tied?' she murmured sceptically, love and laughter bubbling from her as she hugged him fiercely. 'I can't say I have any complaints.'

'That's because you've no idea of the sort of things I'm capable of saying to you once my tongue's really loosened...all of them loving and...Jennifer,' he chuckled warningly, 'you've started going all gooey-eyed on me.'

She clung to him, protesting as he began extricating

himself from her arms, the love dancing openly in his eyes even as they teased.

'Tell me, do you wish to bring your things?' he demanded huskily, 'or shall I simply sling you over my shoulder and carry you home as you are?'

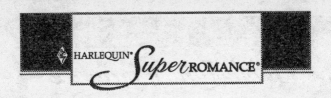

...there's more to the story!

Superromance.
A *big* satisfying read about unforgettable characters. Each month we offer *six* very different stories that range from family drama to adventure and mystery, from highly emotional stories to romantic comedies—and much more! Stories about people you'll believe in and care about. Stories too compelling to put down....

Our authors are among today's *best* romance writers. You'll find familiar names and talented newcomers. Many of them are award winners— and you'll see why!

If you want the biggest and best in romance fiction, you'll get it from Superromance!

Emotional, Exciting, Unexpected...

HARLEQUIN®
*M*akes any time special ®

HARLEQUIN®
INTRIGUE

WE'LL LEAVE YOU BREATHLESS!

If you've been looking for thrilling tales of contemporary passion and sensuous love stories with taut, edge-of-the-seat suspense—then you'll love Harlequin Intrigue!

Every month, you'll meet four new heroes who are guaranteed to make your spine tingle and your pulse pound. With them you'll enter into the exciting world of Harlequin Intrigue— where your life is on the line and so is your heart!

THAT'S INTRIGUE— ROMANTIC SUSPENSE AT ITS BEST!

HARLEQUIN®

Makes any time special ®

From rugged lawmen and valiant knights to defiant heiresses and spirited frontierswomen, Harlequin Historicals will capture your imagination with their dramatic scope, passion and adventure.

*Harlequin Historicals...
they're too good to miss!*